REVISED S1

for MEI Structured Mathematics

Author
Stella Dudzic

Series Editor
Roger Porkess

HODDER
EDUCATION
AN HACHETTE UK COMPANY

The Publishers would like to thank the following for permission to reproduce copyright material:

Acknowledgements

p. 5 Bablake weather station, Table showing monthly average temperature in the Centigrade in Coventry, reproduced by permission of Bablake School; **p. 26** OFCOM, Oftel survey of mobile phone use in May 2003; **p. 96** Office for National Statistics, Table showing Number of people per 1000 marrying, © Crown copyright, reproduced by permission.

Every effort has been made to trace all copyright holders, but if any have been inadvertently overlooked the Publishers will be pleased to make the necessary arrangements at the first opportunity.

Although every effort has been made to ensure that website addresses are correct at time of going to press, Hodder Education cannot be held responsible for the content of any website mentioned in this book. It is sometimes possible to find a relocated web page by typing in the address of the home page for a website in the URL window of your browser.

Hachette UK's policy is to use papers that are natural, renewable and recyclable products and made from wood grown in sustainable forests. The logging and manufacturing processes are expected to conform to the environmental regulations of the country of origin.

Orders: please contact Bookpoint Ltd, 130 Milton Park, Abingdon, Oxon OX14 4SB. Telephone: (44) 01235 827720. Fax: (44) 01235 400454. Lines are open 9.00 – 5.00, Monday to Saturday, with a 24-hour message answering service. Visit our website at www.hoddereducation.co.uk

© Stella Dudzic, Roger Porkess, 2008
First published in 2008 by
Hodder Education,
An Hachette UK company
338 Euston Road
London NW1 3BH

Impression number   6
Year   2013

Dynamic Learning Student Online website © Stella Dudzic, Roger Porkess, 2008; with contributions from Danielle Veall; developed by Infuze Limited; cast: Tom Frankland, Gina Walker; recorded at Alchemy Soho.

Typeset in 12/14 Helvetica by Pantek Arts Ltd, Maidstone, Kent.
Printed in India

A catalogue record for this title is available from the British Library

ISBN: 978 0 340 95743 1

Contents

Introduction

Welcome to this Revision Guide for the MEI Statistics 1 unit!

The book is organised into 20 sections covering the various topics in the syllabus. They follow essentially the same order as the textbook. A typical section is about four pages long; the first three pages contain essential information and key worked examples covering the topic.

The last page in each section has questions for you to answer so that you can be sure that you have really understood the topic. There is a multiple-choice exercise and an exam-style question. If you are to gain the greatest possible benefit from the book, and so do your best in the Statistics 1 exam, you should work through these for yourself and then refer to the accompanying website to check your answers.

The multiple-choice questions cover the basic ideas and techniques. It is really important that you work through them carefully; guessing will do you no good at all. When you have decided on the answer you think is right, enter it on the website. If you are right, it tells you so and gives the full solution; check that your answer wasn't just a fluke. If your choice is not right, the website gives you advice about your mistake; the possible wrong answers have all been designed to pick out particular common misunderstandings. The explanations on the website are based on the most likely mistakes; even if you make a different mistake, you will usually find enough help to set you on the right path so that you can try again.

When you come onto the exam-style question, write out your best possible answer. Then go to the website. You will find the solution displayed step-by-step, together with someone talking you through it and giving you helpful advice.

So the book contains the essential information to revise for the exam and, critically, also enables you to check that you have understood it properly. That is a recipe for success.

If you don't already have them, you will find the tables you need for the binomial hypothesis tests in the *Companion to Advanced Mathematics and Statistics*.

Finally, a word of warning. This book is designed to be used together with the textbook and not as a replacement for it. This Revision Guide will help you to prepare for the exam but to do really well you also need the deep understanding that comes from the detailed explanations you will find in the textbook.

Good learning and good luck!

Stella Dudzic, Roger Porkess

Where you see the following icon ▶⌐, please refer to the Dynamic Learning Student Online website. Information on how to access this website is printed on the inside front cover of the book.

Accompanying books

MEI Structured Mathematics Statistics 1 S1   ISBN 978 0 340 81399 7

Companion to Advanced Mathematics and Statistics   ISBN 978 0 340 95923 7

Exploring data

Stem-and-leaf diagrams and shapes of distributions

A ABOUT THIS TOPIC

Stem-and-leaf diagrams (also called *stemplots*) provide a quick way to use data to visualise the shape of the distribution. Stem-and-leaf diagrams are 'assumed knowledge' for the S1 module. This means that you will not be asked a question that just tests your understanding of stem-and-leaf diagrams but they can be used in questions on more advanced statistics. Describing distributions using skewness is tested in S1. It is important that you understand what the different diagram shapes mean so that you can get a quick idea of what a statistical diagram is telling you.

R REMEMBER

- Mean, median and mode from GCSE (these are also revised in the next section).

K KEY FACTS

- You can use a stem-and-leaf diagram for discrete or continuous data (see next section for more about types of data).
- A stem-and-leaf diagram shows the shape of the distribution as well as keeping the original data values.
- A back-to-back stem-and-leaf diagram is useful for comparing two sets of data.
- The position of the 'tail' of the data shows you the kind of *skewness*.

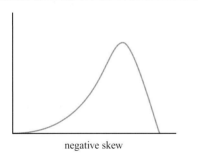
negative skew

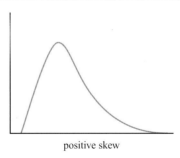
positive skew

- For a negatively skewed distribution, usually median > mean. For a positively skewed distribution, usually median < mean (see next section for more about median and mean).

Stem-and-leaf diagrams

EXAMPLE 1

The heights (in cm) of a sample of girls are shown below. Show them on an appropriate stem-and-leaf diagram.

165	169	136	161	159	140	156	151	170	140
162	175	136	137	152	161	158	172	146	140
153	155	172	162	154	157	161	164	124	123

SOLUTION

The first step is to decide what to use as the stems. For the data in this question, using the number of 'tens' as the stem and the 'units' as the leaf will be appropriate.

```
12 | 4 3
13 | 6 6 7
14 | 0 6 0 0
15 | 3 5 9 2 6 4 1 8 7
16 | 5 9 1 2 1 2 1 4
17 | 0 5 2 2
```

> Although you want the leaves to be in order, you may find it more accurate to do a rough stem-and-leaf diagram first then order the leaves on a final version.

> If you do a rough diagram first in an exam, remember to cross it out when you have drawn your final version, to make it clear which one you want to be marked.

> A stem-and-leaf diagram needs a scale, or key, to say what the numbers stand for. You should include the units of measurement.

```
12 | 3 4
13 | 6 6 7
14 | 0 0 0 6
15 | 1 2 3 4 5 6 7 8 9
16 | 1 1 1 2 2 4 5 9
17 | 0 2 2 5
```

Scale
15 | 1 represents 151 cm

A ADVICE

You are expected to put the 'leaves' in order in a stem-and-leaf diagram (this is called a sorted stem-and-leaf diagram). Putting the leaves in order allows you to use it to find the median (see the next section for more about this).

Stretching a stem-and-leaf diagram

Sometimes there are so many 'leaves' on some lines of the stem-and-leaf diagram that it is difficult to see the overall picture. In these cases, you can use two lines for each 'stem', as shown in the following diagram. This has data on the wealth of 100 of the richest people in the world in the year 2000.

```
 4* | 3 3 3 3 3 3 3 3 4 4 4
 4  | 5 5 5 5 5 6 7 7 7 8 8 9
 5* | 0 0 0 0 1 1 1 2 2 4
 5  | 5 5 5 5 7 7 7 8 9
 6* | 1 1 2 3 3 3 4 4
 6  | 5 6 6 6 7 9
 7* | 0 0 0 1 4 4
 7  | 5 7 8 9
 8* | 0 0 3
 8  | 6
 9* | 0 0 1 3 4
 9  |
10* |
10  | 7
11* | 2 3
11  | 5 9
12* | 1
12  | 6 8

HIGH  15.2, 15.8
```

Scale
4 | 5 represents $4.5 billion

> The first row for each stem has the leaves 0 to 4 inclusive and the second has 5 to 9.

> You need to include all the branches, even those with no leaves.

> Very high (or low) values can be listed separately at the end (or start) of any stem-and-leaf diagram. You should not have more than a couple of these.

Shapes of distributions

If a distribution is not symmetrical, it is skewed. You can see this from the shape of the histogram or frequency polygon. You can also see the shape from a stem-and-leaf diagram.

[handwritten note: See chance of numerical values in AQA book]

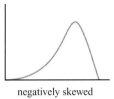

negatively skewed

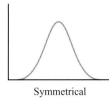

Symmetrical

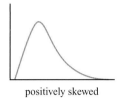

positively skewed

R   RULE

The position of the 'tail' shows you the kind of skewness. The following results usually apply.
For a negatively skewed distribution, median > mean.
For a positively skewed distribution, median < mean.

The 'peak' in a frequency diagram is the mode. A *unimodal* distribution has one mode; a *bimodal* distribution has two modes (if they are not next to each other, one of the modes may have a higher frequency than the other).

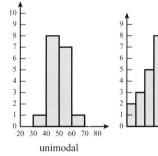

unimodal   bimodal

Back-to-back stem-and-leaf diagrams

Back-to-back stem-and-leaf diagrams are useful for comparing two sets of data, as shown in the following example.

EXAMPLE 2

The stem-and-leaf diagram below shows the heights of a sample of children, with boys and girls shown separately.

> To help you see the skew, you can turn the diagram on its side, with the smallest stem on the left.

⚠ Notice that the leaves are ordered with the smallest near the stem.

```
              Boys  |    | Girls
          7 4 0  | 12 | 3 4
        8 6 5 4  | 13 | 6 6 7
    8 8 5 5 5 1  | 14 | 0 0 0 6
9 7 7 3 3 3 2 0  | 15 | 1 2 3 4 5 6 7 8 9
    8 7 5 3 1 0  | 16 | 1 1 1 2 2 4 5 9
            6 1  | 17 | 0 2 2 5
            8 0  | 18 |
```

Scale 0 | 15 | 1
represents 1.5 m
for boys; 1.51 m
for girls

A   ADVICE

- Notice that the heights for the girls are the same as in the first stem-and-leaf diagram in this section but this time the units are metres not centimetres; the shortest girl is 1.23 m tall.
- Notice that the stem-and-leaf diagram has no decimal points. You look at the scale to find out where they should go.

i) Write down the height of the tallest boy in the sample.
ii) Compare the shapes of the two distributions from this sample.

SOLUTION

i) The tallest boy is 1.88 m tall.

ii) The heights of the boys are slightly more spread out than for the girls. Both distributions are unimodal and the modal group is the same for each (150–159 cm).

The girls' heights are slightly negatively skewed but the boys' heights are more symmetrically distributed.

LINKS

Statistics — Median and quartiles (S1), Histograms (S1), Box-and-whisker plots (S1).

Test Yourself

Data for **questions 1 and 2**:

| 0.90 | 0.57 | 0.78 | 0.74 | 1.26 | 1.08 | 0.96 | 0.43 | 1.17 |
| 0.87 | 1.07 | 0.68 | 0.80 | 1.04 | 0.86 | 0.95 | 1.12 | 1.02 |

The nicotine content in mg for each of a sample of cigarettes is shown above. Put the data into a stem-and-leaf diagram.

1 What is the stem for 1.26?

  A 1   B 6   C 2   D 12   E 1.2

2 What is the shape of the distribution?

  A Positively skewed   B Negatively skewed   C Symmetrical
  D Bimodal   E None of these

3 The stem-and-leaf diagram below shows the foot lengths in mm of a sample of 3 year old boys.

```
14 | 1 1 3 3 3 4 4 5 6 6 6 7 7 7 7 7 8 8 9 9 9 9 9
15 | 0 0 0 0 0 1 1 1 1 1 1 2 3 3 4 4 4 4 4 4 5 5 5 5 5 5 6 6 6 6 7 7 7 7 7 7 7 8 8 8 8 8 8 9 9
16 | 0 0 0 1 1 1 1 1 2 3 3 3 3 4 4 4 4 5 5 6 7 7 8 8 9 9
17 | 6 7
```

The diagram is to be 'stretched' so that there are two rows for each stem. Four of the statements below are false and one is true. Which one is true?

  A The scale is missing on this diagram and it should be '14 | 1 represents 14.1'.
  B The leaf for the measurement 145 mm will be on the top row.
  C You will only need one row in the new diagram for the stem 17.
  D The stem on the top row will be 14*.
  E 'Stretching' the diagram makes it harder to find the median.

4 The heights (in cm) of a sample of children are shown below. Put them into a stretched, back-to-back stem-and-leaf diagram with the boys on the left and the girls on the right.

Boys	137	137	140	140	141	141	146	136	135	149	154	141	142	145	146	153	134	134	138	138	139	139
Girls	138	141	143	144	144	146	149	152	133	138	140	141	141	141	144	147	152	153	134	135	137	138

Four of the statements below are false and one is true. Which one is true?
A The distribution of boys' heights is positively skewed.
B In both parts of the diagram, the leaf for 140 is shown to the left of the leaf for 141.
C A stretched diagram is needed because it is hard to fit on the page otherwise.
D If there had been a girl of height 180 cm, several rows would need to be added to the diagram.
E The diagram shows that, on average, boys are taller than girls.

Exam-Style Question ▶L

The table below shows the monthly average temperature in °C in Coventry for January and February near to the turns of the 20th and 21st centuries.

1896–1905	4.7	1.1	6.1	5.2	4.3	3.2	5.0	4.2	3.8	3.2
	4.3	5.5	4.5	5.0	2.5	2.3	1.3	7.1	3.4	5.5
1996–2005	4.1	2.2	5.1	5.8	5.4	3.2	5.4	4.2	5.1	5.9
	2.6	6.8	7.3	5.1	5.8	4.7	7.0	3.9	5.5	4.2

(Data from Bablake weather station)

i) Draw a back-to-back stem-and-leaf diagram to compare the temperatures for 1896–1905 with 1996–2005.

ii) Use your diagram to compare the temperatures. Does it show evidence of global warming?

Types of data and measures of central tendency

A ABOUT THIS TOPIC

Working with statistics is about making sense of data. It is important to know what kind of data you have so that you can use appropriate techniques to help do this. Averages are often used in everyday life so you need to understand them thoroughly. Averages are sometimes called 'measures of central tendency'.

Most of this section (apart from the mid-range) is 'assumed knowledge' for the S1 module; this means that you will not be asked a question that just tests your understanding of mean, median, mode or types of data but they can be used in questions on more advanced statistics.

R REMEMBER

- Putting numbers in order (including decimals and negative numbers) from GCSE.

- Categorical or qualitative data are not numerical.
- Numerical or quantitative data can be subdivided into discrete or continuous.
- *Continuous* data may take any values; these are usually within a range.
- *Discrete* data may only take certain separate values, for example whole numbers.
- The mean (symbol $\bar{x}$) is found by adding the data values and dividing by the number of values. That is, $\bar{x} = \dfrac{\sum x}{n}$.
- The *median* is the middle value when the data are put in order.
- The *mode* is the most common item of data (modal class is used for grouped data).
- The *mid-range* is halfway between the lowest and highest data items.

Types of data

Categorical or *qualitative* data are in categories; they are not numerical. Examples include eye colour, breed of dog and favourite type of book.

Numerical or *quantitative* data consist of numbers.

An upper case letter is often used to stand for a phrase describing what is being investigated. For example, X might stand for 'the number of heads when tossing five coins' or H might stand for 'the height of the child'. A lower case letter stands for the numerical value it takes, so for example, $x = 3$ or $h = 1.24$ m.

Continuous variables are measured on a scale; for example length, weight, temperature. For any two possible values, you can always find another possible value between them.

In practice, continuous data are always rounded because there is a limit to how accurately they can be measured.

Discrete variables are often just whole numbers; for example, the number of children in a family; but they need not be. For example, scores for some sports, such as the half-pipe snowboarding competition in the 2006 Winter Olympics, have been given in steps of 0.1.

Measures of central tendency (averages)

A measure of central tendency is a single value that is used to represent a set of data. They are sometimes called averages and are useful for comparing sets of data. For example, teachers might compare classes of students by looking at the average test mark for each class.

Mean

The mean is often referred to as 'the average' in everyday speech. It is worked out by adding up the data values and dividing by the number of values. This can be written as the formula:

$$\bar{x} = \frac{\sum_{i=1}^{n} x_i}{n}$$

where

- $\bar{x}$ stands for the mean.
- The data items are $x_1, x_2, \ldots x_n$; x_i is a typical, or general, data item.
- The Greek letter sigma $\left(\sum\right)$ means 'the sum of'. It gives the total of all the data.
- The number of data items is n.

The formula is often written more simply as:

$$\bar{x} = \frac{\sum x}{n} .$$

EXAMPLE 1

The part-time weekly earnings of nine students are shown below. Find the mean.

£10.28 £30.00 £49.20 £29.50 £0.00 £35.10 £58.50 £39.00 £20.00

SOLUTION

$\sum x$

$$\text{Mean} = \frac{10.28 + 30 + 49.20 + 29.50 + 0 + 35.10 + 58.5 + 39 + 20}{9} = \frac{271.58}{9}$$

n

The mean is £30.18 (nearest penny).

Remember to include units.

The mean is a 'fair shares' average; the value you calculated above is the same as you would get working out how much each person would receive if they all shared their earnings equally among themselves.

The mean can be affected by one unusually large (or small) value but it uses all the data and you can work out the total from it.

A ADVICE

It is sensible to use a calculator to do the working but it is easy to type in a wrong number so, in an examination, you should at least write down enough working to show that you are trying to add the data and divide by the number of them. In the example above, write down 271.58 ÷ 9.
You should round your final answer sensibly.

EXAMPLE 2

There are 16 students in a class. 15 of them measure their pulse rates and find the mean is 65. The sixteenth student measures his pulse rate the following lesson; it is 120. What is the mean pulse rate for all 16 students?

mean = $\frac{\text{total}}{n}$ so

total = $n \times$ mean

SOLUTION

The total for the 15 students is $15 \times 65 = 975$.
The total for all 16 students is $975 + 120 = 1095$.
The mean for all 16 students is $1095 \div 16 = 68.4375 = 68.44$ (2 d.p.).

Median

The median is the middle value when the data items are put in order. If there is an even number of data values, there will be two middle values; the median is halfway between them.

A ADVICE

Even if all the data are whole numbers, the mean need not be.

EXAMPLE 3

Find the median of the earnings in example 1.

SOLUTION

Putting the values in order:

£0.00 £10.28 £20.00 £29.50 £30.00 £35.10 £39.00 £49.20 £58.50

The median is £30.

This is the middle one.

The median is £30.
If a tenth student, with weekly earnings of £60, joins the group, the ordered data are:

£0.00 £10.28 £20.00 £29.50 £30.00 £35.10 £39.00 £49.20 £58.50 £60.00

These are the middle ones.

The median is halfway between £30 and £35.10; that is, the median = £32.55.

Mode

The mode is the most commonly occurring value. There can be more than one mode, or there might not be a mode. The mode can be used for categorical data; the other measures of central tendency cannot.

A ADVICE

To find the number halfway between two numbers, add them and divide the answer by 2.
This can be used when finding the mid-range too.

Mid-range

The mid-range is halfway between the largest and smallest data values. It is very easy to work out but can be very unrepresentative if there is an unusually large (or small) data value.

EXAMPLE 4

Find the mid-range of the earnings of the nine students in example 1.

SOLUTION

Mid-range = $\frac{0 + 58.50}{2} = £29.25$

The mid-range is a measure of central tendency. Be careful not to confuse it with the range, which is a measure of spread.

A ADVICE

All the measures of central tendency produce a value that represents the whole set of data. If you get an answer for an average of numerical data that is either larger than the largest value in the set or smaller than the smallest value, you know you have made a mistake somewhere in your calculations.

Deciding which average to use

- The mean and the mid-range are affected by one very large (or small) data value.
- The mean allows you to work out the total of the data and uses all the values.
- The median is not affected by extreme data values.
- The mid-range is easy to calculate and gives the value midway between the highest and lowest values; it is useful if unusual data values are unlikely.
- The mode gives the most likely value to occur; it can be used for categorical data.
- For symmetrical, unimodal data the mean, median, mode and mid-range are all equal.

LINKS

Statistics

Measures of spread (S1), Averages from frequency distributions (S1).

Test Yourself

1 The morning temperature, in °C, on ten consecutive days is as follows:

   −5.3   2.7   −0.3   4.8   −3.3   3.4   2.2   −0.5   0.4   3.9

   What is the median temperature (in °C)?
   A 0.05   B 0.4   C 0.8   D 0.9   E 1.3

2 A group of students were asked how many books they had in their room and gave answers as follows:

   5   5   3   2   1   3   2   57   2   9   3   8

   Four of the following statements are false and one is true. Which one is true?
   A The mode is 2.5.
   B The mean should not be used for this data because it is impossible to have 8.3333… books.
   C There is no limit to the number of books a student could have so the data are continuous.
   D The median, which is 3, is a good average to use as it is unaffected by the large value of 57.
   E The mid-range is 56 ÷ 2 = 28.

3 A class of students consists of 9 girls and 20 boys. The mean weight of the girls is 53 kg; the mean weight of the boys is 61 kg. What is the mean weight for the whole class?
   A 3.9 kg   B 55.5 kg   C 57 kg   D 58.5 kg   E 848.5 kg

4 A teacher has to choose someone from a class to represent them in a regional spelling competition. They have regular spelling tests (marked out of 10) in the class and two students, who have taken all 20 of the class tests, are willing to represent the class. Information about their average scores in the class tests is shown to the right. Four of the following statements are true and one is false. Which one is false?

	Mark	Lucy
Mean	6.8	7.6
Mode	8	6

A Because there were 20 class tests, each of them must have scored their mode more than twice.

B Their means show that Mark scores less than 7 half the time and Lucy scores more than 7 half the time.

C The distribution of Mark's scores cannot be positively skewed or symmetrical.

D For a short competition, Mark is a better choice than Lucy as his higher mode shows that he is more likely to do well.

E For a long competition, Lucy is a better choice than Mark as her higher mean shows that her total score is higher than his.

Exam-Style Question ⊃L

The trustees of a charity are going to appoint a full-time manager. They decide to pay the manager the same as the average of the trustees' earnings. The annual incomes of the trustees are given in the list below (in pounds):

22 000   19 800   8 800   38 500   13 200   55 000   45 000   15 540   14 300

Calculate:

i) a) the mean

    b) the median

    c) the mid-range.

ii) An additional trustee is appointed; her income is lower than that of any of the other trustees. Explain how this additional data item affects each of the averages you calculated in part i).

Frequency distributions and their averages

A ABOUT THIS TOPIC

Averages are very useful for summarising and comparing large sets of data. The data are usually presented as frequency tables. Most of this section is 'assumed knowledge' for the S1 unit. This means that you will not be asked a question that just tests your understanding of mean, median, mode but they can be used in questions on more advanced statistics.

R REMEMBER

- Frequency tables and rounding from GCSE.
- Measures of central tendency from S1.

K KEY FACTS

- For data in a frequency table, the mean is calculated using $\bar{x} = \dfrac{\sum xf}{n}$ where f is the frequency of the data value x.
- For a grouped frequency table, you can only calculate an estimate of the mean as you do not know the exact data values. The mid-point of each group is used when doing this.
- For an ungrouped frequency table, you can find the median. The median is the value of the $\dfrac{n+1}{2}$th data item (they are already in order in the frequency table). You can find which group the median is in for a grouped frequency table in the same way.
- The mode is the item with the highest frequency in an ungrouped frequency table.
- The modal class is the group with the highest frequency in a grouped frequency table (if it has equal width groups).
- The mid-range is easy to calculate from an ungrouped frequency table. For a grouped frequency table, you can only find an estimate as you do not know for certain what the highest and lowest values are.

Averages from an ungrouped frequency table

> If a data value has frequency zero, this means it did not occur. There were no games with 6 or 7 goals.

EXAMPLE 1

The table below shows the number of goals scored by the winning team (or the goals scored by either team in the case of a draw) for a sample of league football matches. Work out the mode, mid-range, median and mean.

Number of goals	0	1	2	3	4	5	6	7	8
Frequency	4	21	22	15	8	3	0	0	1

A ADVICE

In a frequency table for numerical data, there are two sets of numbers. The frequency tells you how often each value occurred; the other numbers are the data values that you are dealing with. Understanding this will help you avoid some of the common mistakes made when working with frequency tables.

It is easy to see that the **mode** is 2 goals, because this happened 22 times (the highest frequency).

It is also easy to work out the **mid-range** because you can see that the highest value is 8 and the lowest value is 0. So the mid-range is 4 goals.

To find the **median** from a frequency table, start by adding a column for cumulative frequency to the table.

> The cumulative frequency is 'the total frequency so far'.

> The data are the number of goals and these are in order in the table.

Number of goals	Frequency	Cumulative frequency
0	4	4
1	21	25
2	22	47
3	15	62
4	8	70
5	3	73
6	0	73
7	0	73
8	1	74

> $25 + 22 = 47$ (adding the frequency to a previous cumulative frequency).

> 74 is the total frequency for this table.

There are 74 data values in total. The median is in position number $\frac{74+1}{2} = 37.5$; this means it is halfway between the 37th and 38th data values. The cumulative frequency column shows you that both the 37th and 38th values are 2 goals, so the median is 2 goals.

R RULE

If there are n data values, in order, the **median** is in position number $\frac{n+1}{2}$; if this is not a whole number, it means that you will be finding the point midway between two values.

To find the **mean** from a frequency table, you will need an additional column for working.

> It will help you set out your working if you label the data column x and the frequency column f.

Number of goals, x	Frequency, f	$x \times f$
0	4	0
1	21	21
2	22	44
3	15	45
4	8	32
5	3	15
6	0	0
7	0	0
8	1	8
Total	74	165

> This 0 means that the four values of 0 in the table add up to 0.

> This 32 means that the eight values of 4 in the table add up to 32.

> The total frequency gives you the number of data values (74 in this case).

> The total number of goals is 165.

$$\text{Mean} = \frac{\text{Total goals}}{\text{Total matches}} = \frac{165}{74} = 2.229\ 729 \ldots = 2.23 \text{ (3 s.f.)}$$

Averages from a grouped frequency table

For the **mean**, the working is like that for an ungrouped frequency table. However, you do not know all the individual data values so you use the mid-point for each group as an estimate of all the values in it. This means that your eventual answer is an estimate of the mean.

A **ADVICE**

When working out the median or mean from a frequency table, you will often find it easier to have the data values going down the page, rather than across the page.

EXAMPLE 2

The table below shows the time before the first goal of the match was scored for a sample of league football matches. Find the mean, mid-range and median values.

SOLUTION

It would not make sense to state the **modal class** for this table because there are some groups wider than others; if they were the same width, things could look different.

Time, in minutes	Frequency, f	Mid-point, x	$x \times f$
1–10	9	5.5	49.5
11–20	12	15.5	186.0
21–30	10	25.5	255.0
31–45	19	38.0	722.0
46–60	11	53.0	583.0
61–70	6	65.5	393.0
71–80	3	75.5	226.5
81–90	0	85.5	0
Total	70	**Total**	2415.0

The working is the same as for an ungrouped table **except** that you are working with the mid-point of each group as an estimate of the values in that group.

There are 70 data items with an estimated total of 2415.

Do not add up the mid-points column; the answer would not mean anything.

$$\text{Mean} = \frac{2415}{70} = 34.5$$

 The times have been rounded before being put into the frequency table. The 11–20 minute group is really $10\frac{1}{2} \leqslant$ time $< 20\frac{1}{2}$ minutes; in this case the mid-point would be the same so it does not make a difference. But be especially careful when working with ages as they are always rounded down. 11–20 years would really be $11 \leqslant$ age < 21 years, with a mid-point of 16.0.

A ADVICE

- It can be easy to go wrong when working out the mean from a frequency table; always look back at the data to see whether your final answer is a reasonable average.
- It is possible to enter data from a frequency table into some calculators and get the mean but if you do this in an exam, show no working and make a mistake you will get no marks. Showing your working in a table in the exam helps to ensure you will get some marks even if you go wrong.
- Sometimes exam questions tell you the total of the data values to cut down the time you spend working this out.

To find the **mid-range**, you need to know the highest and lowest data values. You know the lowest data value for the table of times to the first goal is in the 1–10 minutes group and the highest value is in the 71–80 minutes group. You could use 1 and 80 to estimate the mid-range.

The **median** is found by using a cumulative frequency graph; this is revised on page 38.

LINKS

Mechanics	Centre of mass (M2).
Statistics	Measures of spread (S1), Cumulative frequency diagrams (S1), Discrete random variables (S1).

Test Yourself

A sample of students are asked how many school dinners they ate in the past week with the following results. These data are used in **questions 1, 2 and 3**.

Number of dinners eaten	0	1	2	3	4	5
Frequency	7	10	10	12	21	18

1 Four of the statements below are false and one is true. Which one is true?
  A The mid-range is 2.5.
  B The mode is 10.
  C The number of students in the sample was 6.
  D The number of students in the sample was 15.
  E The distribution shows positive skewness.

2 Find the median.
  A 2.5   B 3   C 3.5   D 4   E 39.5

3 Find the mean.
  A 2.5   B 3   C 3.1   D 13   E 40

The waist measurements of a sample of boys are shown below. These data are used in **questions 4 and 5**.

Waist (cm)	50–59	60–69	70–79	80–89	90–109
Frequency	2	45	80	19	7

4 Find an estimate of the mean.
  A 73.5 cm   B 73.7 cm   C 74.2 cm   D 75.5 cm   E 70–79 cm

5 Four of the statements below are false and one is true. Which one is true?
  A A good estimate of the mid-range is 30 cm.
  B A good estimate of the mid-range is 70 cm.
  C A good estimate of the mid-range is 84 cm.
  D The median is 74.5 cm.
  E The median is somewhere in the group 70–79 cm.

Exam-Style Question ⊃L

The table below shows the ages of students on a course at university.

Ages	17–21	22–26	27–31	32–40
Frequency	13	11	3	4

i)   Alan is calculating an estimate of their mean age. He starts by saying that the mid-point of the first group is 19. Is this correct? Explain your answer.

ii) Find an estimate of the mean age.

iii) Why is your answer only an estimate?

iv) One of the students who was put in the last group in the table should not have been put in this group as he is 55 years old. Find a better estimate of the mean, taking account of this information.

Measures of spread

A ABOUT THIS TOPIC

An average summarises the data with a single value but it is also important to know how spread out the data are. There are different measures of spread (also called measures of dispersion) and it is important to understand them to help you make more sense of data.

R REMEMBER

- How to find the mean from S1.

K KEY FACTS

- The range = maximum data value − minimum data value.
- The sum of squares, S_{xx}, is used in calculating several measures of spread.
- $S_{xx} = \sum(x - \bar{x})^2 = \sum x^2 - n\bar{x}^2$.
- Mean square deviation, $msd = \dfrac{S_{xx}}{n}$.
- Root mean square deviation, $rmsd = \sqrt{msd} = \sqrt{\dfrac{S_{xx}}{n}}$.
- Variance, $s^2 = \dfrac{S_{xx}}{n-1}$.
- Standard deviation, $s = \sqrt{variance} = \sqrt{\dfrac{S_{xx}}{n-1}}$.

The need for a measure of dispersion

Imagine you are deciding where to go on holiday in July. You have narrowed it down to two destinations, each with an average July temperature of 27 °C. Knowing that one destination has a minimum July temperature of 21 °C and a maximum of 32 °C while the other has a minimum of 10 °C and a maximum of 41°C would provide you with useful additional information.

The range

The range is the simplest measure of spread; it is calculated by subtracting the smallest data value from the largest data value. For the two holiday destinations above, the ranges would be:

32 – 21 = 11 °C and 41 – 10 = 31 °C.

The range is affected by one very large (or small) data value. Other measures of dispersion are less prone to this. Interquartile range is revised on page 36; the other measures of dispersion in this section rely on measuring how far the data are from the mean.

 Be careful not to confuse the range and the mid-range. The range is a measure of spread but the mid-range is an average.

The sum of squares (of deviations from the mean)

All four measures of dispersion considered in the next sections use the sum of squares of deviations from the mean.
$S_{xx} = \sum(x - \bar{x})^2 = \sum x^2 - n\bar{x}^2$. The first format of the formula makes it easier to understand what is being calculated but the second involves less work when doing the calculation. $(x - \bar{x})$ is the distance of a data item from the mean. Some data items will be above the mean, others will be below it. Squaring $(x - \bar{x})$ makes all these values positive. The measures of dispersion that use S_{xx} are measuring how far the data items are from the mean. If they are all near the mean, the data are not very spread out.

EXAMPLE 1

Some students are playing a dice game. The following data show how many times each of them had to throw a die before getting a 6.

3　6　1　4　1　12　4　7

Calculate S_{xx}.

SOLUTION

$$\bar{x} = \frac{3+6+1+4+1+12+4+7}{8} = \frac{38}{8} = 4.75$$ ← First find the mean.

$$\sum x^2 = 3^2 + 6^2 + 1^2 + 4^2 + 1^2 + 12^2 + 4^2 + 7^2 = 272$$

Next find the sum of the squares of the data values.

$$S_{xx} = \sum x^2 - n\bar{x}^2 = 272 - 8 \times 4.75^2$$

$$S_{xx} = 91.5$$

n is the number of data values (8 in this example).

$\sum x^2$ means 'square each data value and add them up'. Do not confuse it with $\left(\sum x\right)^2$ which would mean 'add the data values and square the answer'. These do not give the same result.

If you are asked to calculate the mean square deviation, the root mean square deviation, the variance or the standard deviation, first calculate S_{xx}.

Mean square deviation and root mean square deviation

For example 1, $msd = \dfrac{S_{xx}}{n} = \dfrac{91.5}{8} = 11.4375$

$rmsd = \sqrt{msd} = \sqrt{11.4375} = 3.38$ (2.d.p.).

Each $(x - \bar{x})^2$ is the square of the deviation (from the mean). Adding these gives $S_{xx} = \sum(x - \bar{x})^2 = \sum x^2 - n\bar{x}^2$; dividing by n finds the mean of these squared deviations.

Variance and standard deviation

For example 1, variance $s^2 = \dfrac{S_{xx}}{n-1} = \dfrac{91.5}{7} = 13.071\,428\ldots$

standard deviation, $s = \sqrt{\text{variance}} = \sqrt{13.071\,428\ldots} = 3.62$ (2 d.p.).

Do not round until you have got your final answer. You should work with the unrounded value of the mean. If you are asked to work out variance then round it sensibly, but if the variance is part of your working in finding standard deviation then wait till you have worked that out before rounding, otherwise your answer will be less accurate.

 Some textbooks use n as a divisor for the variance and standard deviation; this is not correct when working with a sample (you will always work with a sample in practice). Wording in exam questions will sometimes be 'sample variance' and 'sample standard deviation'. This means the same as 'variance' and 'standard deviation' when you are working with data. You will find variance and standard deviation for a random variable in a later section.

Working with summaries of data

Sometimes in examination questions you will be given summaries of the data that start you off on your working.

EXAMPLE 2

The table below shows the scores obtained when a die is rolled.

Score	1	2	3	4	5	6
Frequency	10	7	11	11	13	18

For these data, $n = 70$, $\sum x = 274$, $\sum x^2 = 1286$.

Find the sample standard deviation.

A   ADVICE

- Working out the standard deviation from a frequency table is covered in the next section but, since you are given $n, \sum x, \sum x^2$ use them in your working.
- Many scientific calculators have more than one memory. Use the memories to keep exact values of $\bar{x}$, S_{xx} and so on, so that you can use them in later calculations.

SOLUTION

$$\bar{x} = \frac{274}{70} = 3.914285\ldots$$

$$S_{xx} = \sum x^2 - n\bar{x}^2 = 1286 - 70 \times (3.914285\ldots)^2$$

$$S_{xx} = 213.485714\ldots$$

$$s = \sqrt{\frac{S_{xx}}{n-1}} = \sqrt{\frac{213.485714\ldots}{69}}$$

$$s = \sqrt{3.093995\ldots} = 1.758975\ldots$$

$$s = 1.76 \ (3 \text{ s.f.})$$

> Work out the mean first. Remember you will need the unrounded answer for the rest of your working.

> Work out S_{xx} before working out the measure of spread you are asked to calculate.

> Make sure you divide by 69 here, not 70.

⚠ You can enter data into your calculator to get the mean and standard deviation but doing this in an exam means that you risk typing in a wrong value and getting the wrong answer. If you do not show any working you will not get any marks if the answer is wrong.
You could use your calculator to get $n, \sum x, \sum x^2$
and carry the working on from there, as in example 2.

LINKS

Statistics   Interquartile range (S1), Discrete random variables (S1), Mean and variance of random variables (S3), Estimating population variance (S3).

Test Yourself ⟩L

1 The number of goals scored by a football team in a sample of games is:

2   3   5   7   7   1   2

Find S_{xx} for this sample (some of these answers have been rounded).
A 34.53   B 36.857   C 51.735   D 141   E 624.857

2 The heights, in metres, of a sample of children are:

1.33   1.36   1.39   1.40   1.42   1.42   1.50   1.56   1.59   1.61
1.65   1.69

Find the sample standard deviation (all answers are in metres, to 3 s.f.).
A 0.0150   B 0.117   C 0.123   D 0.126   E 5.17

3 A class of students sat a test. Their mean mark was 63. Another student sits the test later and gains a mark of 63. The mean and standard deviation are recalculated to include this mark. Four of the following statements are false and one is true. Which one is true?

A The mean stays the same but there is not enough information to say what happens to the standard deviation.

B There is not enough information to say what happens to the mean or the standard deviation.

C The new mean is the same as before but the standard deviation is lower.

D Both the mean and the standard deviation stay the same.

E Both the mean and the standard deviation are decreased because of the additional mark.

Questions 4 and 5 use the following data. Seven coins are tossed by each of 20 students and the number of heads each time is noted.

3 6 6 4 2 5 5 4 3 2 3 1 3 4 4 4 0 3 4 2

$\sum x = 68$, $\sum x^2 = 276$.

4 Find the mean number of heads obtained from the seven coins.

A 2.86 (3 s.f.)   B 3.4   C 4.06 (3 s.f.)   D 9.71 (3 s.f.)   E 0.294 (3 s.f.)

5 Find the mean square deviation of the number of heads on the coins.

A 1.50 (3 s.f.)   B 1.54 (3 s.f.)   C 2.24   D 2.36 (3 s.f.)   E 13.8

Exam-Style Question 乚

A bakery makes loaves of bread labelled 400 grams. A sample of ten loaves is taken and their weights, in grams, are shown here.

407.0   397.2   412.4   422.8   422.0   427.3   388.2   407.7   421.0   399.1

i)   Find the sample mean and sample variance of the weights.

ii) For the next sample of ten loaves, $\sum x = 3935.7$ and $\sum x^2 = 1598296.4$. Find the mean and variance of this sample.

iii) Comment on your answers for the two samples.

Standard deviation from a frequency table, outliers and linear coding

A ABOUT THIS TOPIC

In this section, you will revise how to work out measures of spread from a frequency table and how to find the mean and standard deviation of a set of data which is related to the original data; this will save you time when calculating these summary measures. Outliers are unusually large, or small, data values. It is useful to be able to recognise them so that you can decide how to deal with them.

R REMEMBER

- How to find the variance and standard deviation from S1.
- How to find the mean from a frequency table from S1.

K KEY FACTS

- For data in a frequency table, $S_{xx} = \sum(x - \bar{x})^2 f = \sum x^2 f - n\bar{x}^2$

- Mean square deviation, $msd = \dfrac{S_{xx}}{n}$

- Root mean square deviation, $rmsd = \sqrt{msd} = \sqrt{\dfrac{S_{xx}}{n}}$

- Variance, $s^2 = \dfrac{S_{xx}}{n-1}$

- Standard deviation, $s = \sqrt{variance} = \sqrt{\dfrac{S_{xx}}{n-1}}$

- A data item may be considered to be an *outlier* if it is more than two standard deviations away from the mean.

- If the variables x and y are related by $y = a + bx$ (a and b constant) then the means are related by $\bar{y} = a + b\bar{x}$ and the standard deviations are related by $s_y = bs_x$. The values of *rmsd* are related in the same way as the values of standard deviations.

Working from a frequency table

The working is similar to that for calculating the mean from a frequency table but you need an additional column to help you calculate S_{xx}.

EXAMPLE 1   The table below shows the number of goals scored by a football team in some of its matches. Find the sample mean and sample standard deviation.

Number of goals	0	1	2	3
Frequency	9	17	10	2

A ADVICE

You can enter data into your calculator to get the mean and standard deviation but doing this in an exam means that you risk typing in a wrong value and getting the wrong answer. If you do not show any working you will not get any marks if the answer is wrong. If you set out your working in a table and write down a number incorrectly you should still get marks for showing your working.

SOLUTION

Number of goals, x	Frequency, f	xf	x^2f
0	9	0	0
1	17	17	17
2	10	20	40
3	2	6	18
Total	38	43	75

Start by rearranging the table with the data downwards and label columns x and f.

You need xf so you can calculate the mean and x^2f so you can calculate S_{xx}.

Remember that adding the numbers in the first column does not give you useful information.

This is n, the total number of data values.

Round your answer for the mean sensibly but keep the unrounded answer in your calculator memory and use it in working.

$$\text{Mean, } \bar{x} = \frac{\sum xf}{\sum f} = \frac{43}{38} = 1.13 \text{ (2 d.p.)}$$

$$S_{xx} = \sum x^2 f - n\bar{x}^2 = 75 - 38 \times (1.131\,578\,...)^2$$

$$S_{xx} = 26.342\,105$$

$$s = \sqrt{\frac{S_{xx}}{n-1}} = \sqrt{\frac{26.342\,105\,...}{37}} = 0.844 \text{ (3 s.f.)}$$

Use the unrounded value for working out standard deviation.

Working from a grouped frequency table

This is the same as for an ungrouped frequency table but you need to find the mid-point of each group first.

Outliers

Outliers are unusually large or unusually small data values. They can occur for a number of reasons; they might be mistakes or they might be genuine data values that happen to be very large or small. There are several rules of thumb for identifying outliers.

R RULE

A data item may be considered to be an outlier if it is more than two standard deviations away from the mean.

EXAMPLE 2

A class are trialling a test. They time how long it takes them to complete it. The mean time is 69.4 minutes and the standard deviation is 11.3 minutes. How high, or low, would a student's time have to be for it to be considered an outlier?

SOLUTION

$\bar{x} + 2s = 69.4 + 2 \times 11.3 = 92$
$\bar{x} - 2s = 69.4 - 2 \times 11.3 = 46.8$

Times which are above 92 minutes or below 46.8 minutes could be considered outliers.

A ADVICE

Sometimes it is obvious that a data item is a mistake. For example, a person 2.75 m tall would be taller than the world's tallest man so such a data item would be incorrect. It should either be ignored or, if possible, corrected. On the other hand, a data item giving the height of a person as 2.21 m could be genuine but, if possible, should be checked.

Linear coding

If the variables x and y are related by $y = a + bx$ (a and b constant) this is a linear relationship because plotting pairs of x and y values on a graph would result in a straight line. The means are related by $\bar{y} = a + b\bar{x}$ and the variances are related by $s_y^2 = b^2 s_x^2$. For standard deviations, $s_y = bs_x$.

EXAMPLE 3

Katrina is working on a geography project with her American penfriend. She measures the outside temperature at 9a.m. over 12 days. The mean is 8.025 °C and the standard deviation is 1.48 °C (3 s.f.). Her American friend needs the mean and standard deviation for the temperatures in degrees Fahrenheit. The Fahrenheit temperature can be found from the Celsius temperature using the formula $F = \frac{9}{5}C + 32$. Find the mean and standard deviation of the Fahrenheit temperatures.

SOLUTION

Mean Fahrenheit temperature, $\bar{F} = \frac{9}{5}\bar{C} + 32$

$$= \frac{9}{5} \times 8.025 + 32 = 46.4 \text{ (3 s.f.)}$$

Standard deviation of Fahrenheit temperatures, $s_F = \frac{9}{5} s_C$

$$= \frac{9}{5} \times 1.48 = 2.66 \text{ (3 s.f.)}$$

Notice whether you are asked for the standard deviation or the variance of related sets of data. For the standard deviation $s_y = bs_x$, but for the variance $s_y^2 = b^2 s_x^2$. The same kind of relationships apply for *rmsd* and *msd*.

Since 1.48 was a rounded value, it makes sense to round this answer too. You can't get an answer that is more accurate than the numbers you worked with.

EXAMPLE 4

There are 25 sweets in a packet of 'Reds and Yellows' and each sweet is either red or yellow. The numbers of red sweets from a sample of packets are given here.

| 11 | 14 | 18 | 12 | 10 | 7 | 14 | 12 | 11 | 15 |

The mean number of red sweets is 12.4 and the variance is 9.156. Find the mean and variance of the number of yellow sweets.

SOLUTION

If the number of red sweets is r and the number of yellow sweets is y then $y = 25 - r$. This is a linear relationship.

$$\bar{y} = 25 - \bar{r} = 25 - 12.4 = 12.6$$
$$s_y^2 = (-1)^2 s_r^2 = 9.156$$

$y = -1r + 25$

> ⚠ If the standard deviation of the number of yellow sweets had been asked for, it would be the same as the standard deviation of the red sweets; it would not be negative, in spite of the multiplier -1. The standard deviation is always positive.

LINKS

Statistics

Interquartile range and box-and-whisker plots (S1), Mean and variance of random variables (S3), Estimating population variance (S3).

Test Yourself

Questions 1 and 2 are about the following data.

A sample of women in their forties are asked how many children they have had.

Number of children	0	1	2	3	4	5	6
Frequency	13	17	38	20	8	3	1

1 Four of the following statements are false and one is true. Which one is true?
A $S_{xx} = 588$
B There were 206 women in the sample.
C $n = 7$
D $S_{xx} = 167.88$ (2 d.p.)
E The mean number of children per woman was 2.06.

2 What is the variance of the number of children per woman (answers to 3 s.f.)?
A 1.28   B 1.29   C 1.64   D 1.65   E 43.0

3 Mr Brown times his bus journey from the railway station to the office. These are the times (in minutes) for 10 journeys:

9   10   12   16   10   1   28   13   9   10

Four of the following statements are false and one is true. Which one is true?
A The time of 28 minutes is an outlier and it should be ignored.
B The mean is not the best measure of central tendency to use for this set of data.
C 28 minutes is probably a misprint for 18 minutes so the 28 should be replaced by 18.
D One minute is not small enough to be an outlier so it is a correct data value.
E If the times had been measured and recorded accurately, there would not be any outliers.

4 An exam has a maximum mark of 150. Candidates score marks with a mean of 86 and a standard deviation of 32. To assist comparison with another exam, these marks (x) are scaled using the formula $y = a + bx$ (a and b are constants). The mean of the new marks is 70 and the standard deviation is 20. What is the maximum of the new marks, y?
A 110   B 129.3 (1 d.p.)   C 172.4   D 198   E 214

Exam-Style Question ⊃L

A teacher is trialling an online multiple choice quiz to test her students' understanding of statistics. The number of questions answered correctly (out of 25) by a sample of 15 students is as follows:

5   12   18   14   25   7   16   16   5   2   22   7   5   14   18

i)   Find the mean and the standard deviation of these data.

ii)   The score (y) is calculated by giving four marks for each question answered correctly and subtracting one mark for each one answered incorrectly. Assuming that no questions are left blank, show that, if x questions are answered correctly, the score is $y = 5x - 25$.

iii) Find the mean and standard deviation of the scores for the 15 students in the sample.

iv)   There are five choices of answer for each question in the quiz. What does it mean to get a negative score?

Data presentation and related measures of centre and spread

2

Appropriate ways of presenting data

ABOUT THIS TOPIC

Being able to understand statistical graphs and use them appropriately is an important skill, not just for your S1 examination, but also so that you can understand statistical information. You are likely to encounter such graphs in the news, in other subjects and also in your future work.

R REMEMBER

- How to draw bar charts and pie charts from GCSE.
- Types of data from S1.

K KEY FACTS

- Vertical line charts are often used for discrete data. The vertical axis shows the frequency.
- Bar charts are often used for categorical data. There should be gaps between the bars.
- A compound bar chart stacks the bars for several sets of data on top of each other so that they can be compared.
- A multiple bar chart puts the bars for several sets of data next to each other so that they can be compared.
- Pie charts can be used for various kinds of data. They show the relationship between the parts of data and the whole data set. If two (or more) pie charts are drawn to compare related sets of data, their areas should be proportional to the totals. That is, you need to make the ratio of the areas the same as the ratio of the totals.

Using statistical diagrams

Statistical diagrams can give a quick visual impression of a whole set of data. It is important to use the right kind of diagram and to draw it correctly so that the impression given is an accurate one. The flow chart on page 27 will help you to make the right choice.

Vertical line charts

A vertical line chart is useful for discrete data; the data need to be in a frequency table first. The vertical axis of the chart shows the frequency. The horizontal axis has an even scale for the data values.

EXAMPLE 1

A sample of female students was asked what shoe size they take, with the following results. Illustrate these data using an appropriate diagram.

Shoe size	$3\frac{1}{2}$	4	$4\frac{1}{2}$	5	$5\frac{1}{2}$	6	$6\frac{1}{2}$	7	$7\frac{1}{2}$	8
Frequency	3	4	4	11	11	8	7	3	4	3

SOLUTION

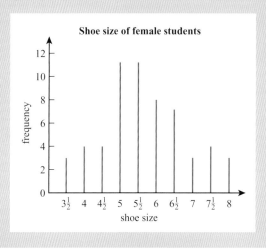

A ADVICE

A vertical line chart emphasises the discrete nature of this data better than a bar chart would because the lines show that the only possible values are $3\frac{1}{2}$, 4, and so on.

Be careful not to confuse a vertical line chart (which shows the frequencies of the data values for a set of discrete data) with a line graph (which shows how a variable is changing over time). An example of a line graph is shown below; some people call it a line chart.

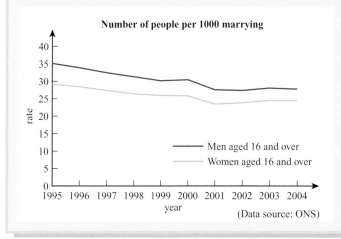

Which diagram to use?

Start in the yellow box towards the centre to help you make a decision about the best diagram to use. Sometimes there is more than one possibility.

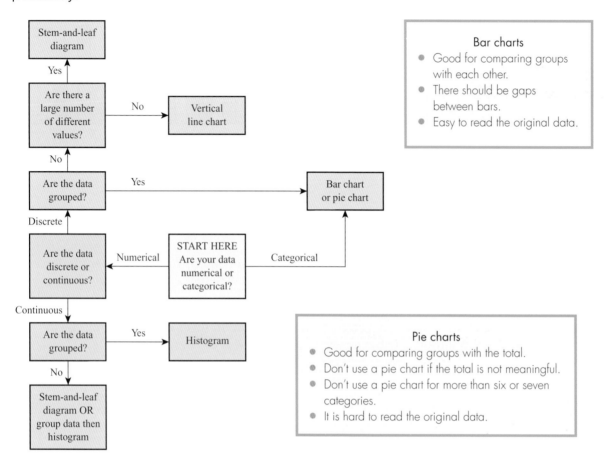

Bar charts
- Good for comparing groups with each other.
- There should be gaps between bars.
- Easy to read the original data.

Pie charts
- Good for comparing groups with the total.
- Don't use a pie chart if the total is not meaningful.
- Don't use a pie chart for more than six or seven categories.
- It is hard to read the original data.

Compound bar charts and multiple bar charts

Compound bar charts and multiple bar charts are used to compare two, or more, sets of similar data, as in the next example.

EXAMPLE 2   A sample of adults was asked which sports they had taken part in during the last month. Illustrate the data with a suitable diagram.

Sport	Walking/ hiking	Snooker	Swimming	Cycling	Football	Keep fit	Other
Men	19	15	13	12	10	8	9
Women	23	4	17	7	1	18	1

SOLUTION

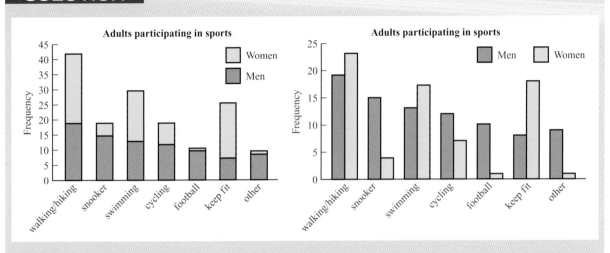

- Either of the charts shown above would be suitable.
- The one on the left is a *compound bar chart*; it is good for comparing the total number of adults for each sport.
- The one on the right is a *multiple bar chart*; it is good for comparing the number of men with the number of women participating in each sport. There is a gap between each group of bars.
- For either type of bar chart, you should have a key showing which colour stands for which set of data. The parts of bars ('women' and 'men' in this example) should be in the same order throughout the bar chart.

Pie charts

If two (or more) pie charts are drawn to compare related sets of data, the ratio of their areas is the same as the ratio of the totals. For example, if data from two surveys are compared where one survey has a sample of 30 items and the other a sample of 120 items, the areas of the circles for the pie charts would be in ratio 30:120 = 1:4. The area of a circle is πr^2, so the radii of the pie charts would be in the ratio $1 : \sqrt{4} = 1 : 2$.

 Spreadsheets can draw many types of statistical diagrams but it is up to you to choose the right kind of diagram.

A ADVICE

If you are drawing a pie chart by hand, check the angles add up to 360°.

 You should only use a pie chart if the total is meaningful. For example, a pie chart is not suitable for data such as in example 2 as some people might take part in more than one sport. Thus the total frequency is not the same as the total number of people.

 LINKS

Statistics   Discrete random variables (S1), Histograms (S1).

Test Yourself

1 A head of year wants to illustrate how many days'
absence each of 6 classes had in a school year.
She needs to decide whether to draw a vertical
line chart, a bar chart or a pie chart. Which of
these kinds of statistical diagram would be well
suited for this purpose?

A Only a vertical line chart
B Only a bar chart
C Only a pie chart
D Either a vertical line chart or a bar chart but not a pie chart
E Either a bar chart or a pie chart but not a vertical line chart

Form	Days absence
10A	217
10B	74
10F	99

2 The table below shows the different types of item on the front page of a local newspaper.

Item	Title	Stories	Adverts	Photos
Area (cm²)	80	441	351	56

A pie chart is to be drawn to show this set of data. What angle will be needed for 'Stories'?

A 140°   B 171°   C 172°   D 176°   E 210°

3 The pie chart illustrates the number of bedrooms in
houses for sale advertised in the *Avonford Star*.
There were 72 houses for sale altogether.
How many had one bedroom?

A 1.8
B 2
C 10
D 50
E Not possible to tell

number of bedrooms

4 Four of the following statements about the graph here are false and one is true. Which
one is true?

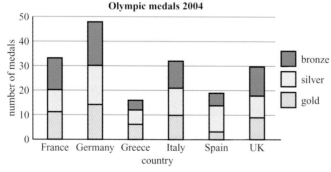

A UK had 30 bronze medals.
B Greece had more silver medals than gold medals.
C France had more silver medals than the UK.
D Germany had more silver medals than gold medals.
E Ranking these countries in order of their number of gold medals gives the same result
as ranking them by their total number of medals.

Exam-Style Question ⟩L

The table below shows the shoe sizes of a sample of Year 1 children.

Shoe size	9	$9\frac{1}{2}$	10	$10\frac{1}{2}$	11	$11\frac{1}{2}$	12	$12\frac{1}{2}$	13	$13\frac{1}{2}$
Number of girls	1	5	7	5	3	3	2	1		
Number of boys			1	1	2	6	8	4	3	1
Total number	1	5	8	6	5	9	10	5	3	1

i) Draw a vertical line chart to show the distribution of the **girls'** shoe sizes.

ii) Describe the shape of the distribution of the girls' shoe sizes.

iii) Draw a separate vertical line chart to show the distribution of the shoe sizes of the **total** sample of children.

iv) Describe the shape of the distribution of shoe sizes in the total sample.

Histograms

A ABOUT THIS TOPIC

Histograms are usually used for displaying continuous data which have been grouped. You may have studied them already at GCSE but do check your understanding to make sure you don't lose marks at A level.

R REMEMBER

- Frequency tables and rounding from GCSE.
- Stem-and-leaf diagrams and median from S1.

K KEY FACTS

- Histograms are usually used for continuous grouped data.
- The horizontal axis is an even scale showing the values of the variable (for example, height, wage, age).
- The vertical axis shows frequency density but its label should be more exact than just 'frequency density'. This can be:
  - either 'frequency per...', for example, 'frequency per 10 cm'
  - or 'frequency density (... per...)', for example, '(people per 5 kg)'.
  - The symbol '/' can be used instead of 'per'.
- Because the horizontal axis is a continuous scale, there are no gaps between bars.
- The frequency represented by a bar is proportional to the area of the bar.
- The median cuts the histogram into two halves of equal area.

2

Histograms for continuous data with equal class widths

EXAMPLE 1

EXAMPLE 1

The birth weights of a sample of babies are given in this table. Draw a histogram to illustrate these data.

Weight (kg)	Frequency
$2.0 \leqslant w < 2.5$	2
$2.5 \leqslant w < 3.0$	13
$3.0 \leqslant w < 3.5$	29
$3.5 \leqslant w < 4.0$	20
$4.0 \leqslant w < 4.5$	11

SOLUTION

Each group is 0.5 kg wide and the frequency is the number of babies so the vertical axis is 'frequency density (babies/0.5 kg)'.

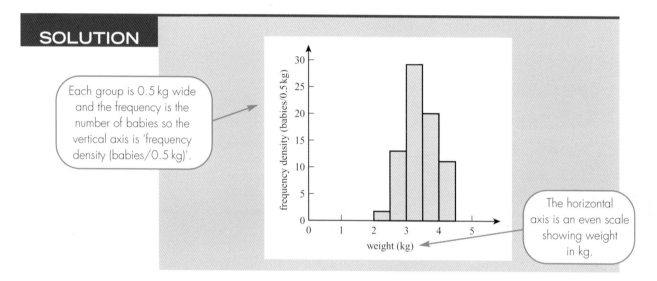

The horizontal axis is an even scale showing weight in kg.

A ADVICE

The vertical axis could be labelled 'frequency per 0.5 kg' instead. If class widths are equal it is not necessary to do any calculations to find frequency density.

Histograms for continuous data with unequal class widths

A ADVICE

Most of the data for example 1 is in the middle of the distribution. Using narrower groups in the middle and wider ones at the edges can help to show an appropriate level of detail.

EXAMPLE 2

The data from example 1 have been grouped differently and are shown in the table on the next page. Draw a histogram with these groups.

SOLUTION

Weight (kg)	Frequency	Class width (kg)	Frequency density (babies/0.5 kg)
$2.0 \leqslant w < 2.5$	2	0.5	2
$2.5 \leqslant w < 3.0$	13	0.5	13
$3.0 \leqslant w < 3.25$	15	0.25	30
$3.25 \leqslant w < 3.5$	14	0.25	28
$3.5 \leqslant w < 3.75$	10	0.25	20
$3.75 \leqslant w < 4.0$	10	0.25	20
$4.0 \leqslant w < 4.5$	11	0.5	11

> Having decided on a standard width of 0.5 kg, the frequency density of any bar with that width is equal to its frequency.

> 15 per 0.25 kg means 30 per 0.5 kg.

A ADVICE

- The last two columns in the table have been added on for working out. It is helpful to write down all the class widths so that you can compare them.
- To calculate frequency density, decide on a 'standard width' for a bar. For this example, you could choose either 0.5 kg or 0.25 kg.

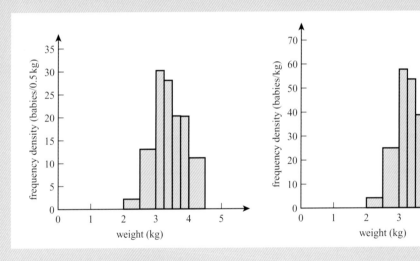

A ADVICE

- Some people prefer always to calculate frequency density by dividing frequency by class width. In this example it would give 'babies/kg' for the frequency density. The histogram is shown on the right. It is the same shape as the one on the left but the vertical axis is different.
- If the frequency density is calculated by frequency divided by class width, this can be called just 'frequency density'.
- The area of a bar in a histogram is proportional to the frequency of the group it represents.

Estimating the median from a histogram

A vertical line at the median would cut the area of the histogram into two equal halves. To find the median, start by finding the area of each bar. The frequency is proportional to the area so you can use the frequency as a measure of the area.

Half the total frequency is $75 \div 2 = 37.5$; this represents the area in front of the median. To get this area you need all of the first three bars and part of the fourth one.

$2 + 13 + 15 = 30$ ◀ —

$37.5 - 30 = 7.5$

> This is the total area of the first three bars.

> This is the area of the part of the fourth bar that is in front of the median.

Bar	Area (frequency)
$2.0 \leqslant w < 2.5$	2
$2.5 \leqslant w < 3.0$	13
$3.0 \leqslant w < 3.25$	15
$3.25 \leqslant w < 3.5$	14
$3.5 \leqslant w < 3.75$	10
$3.75 \leqslant w < 4.0$	10
$4.0 \leqslant w < 4.5$	11
Total	**75**

The fraction of the fourth bar that is needed is $\dfrac{7.5}{14}$ since its total frequency is 14.

3.25   3.5
median

The width of the bar is 0.25 so

$$\frac{7.5}{14} = \frac{d}{0.25}$$

$$d = \frac{0.25 \times 7.5}{14} = 0.13 \,(2\,\text{d.p.})$$

median $= 3.25 + d = 3.25 + 0.13$

median $= 3.38\,\text{kg}$.

> The median is a weight so put units on the final answer.

> The fraction of width is the same as the fraction of area.

A ADVICE

- Don't worry about the units when finding the areas of the bars; they will look after themselves if your scales are correct. Make sure you find the area in the same way for each bar. You can count squares or work out width multiplied by height instead of using the frequency.
- The data have been grouped so you don't know what all the original values were. The final answer will be an estimate of the median.

A ADVICE

Histograms are not usually used for grouped discrete data, but they can be in circumstances when the grouped discrete data can be treated in the same way as grouped continuous data.

⚠ When drawing a histogram for **age**, remember that, for example, a group aged 14–19 years could have people that are only a day short of their 20th birthday so its bar width would be $20 - 14 = 6$.

◻ **LINKS**

Statistics   Probability density function (S3).

Test Yourself >L

1 A sample of students was asked to estimate the length of a line. The data are shown in the table. Four attempts at a histogram for these data are shown below. Three of them are incorrect and one is correct. Which one is correct?

Estimate (cm)	Frequency
$14 \leqslant l < 18$	12
$18 \leqslant l < 22$	7
$22 \leqslant l < 24$	13
$24 \leqslant l < 26$	7
$26 \leqslant l < 30$	8
$30 \leqslant l < 34$	7
$34 \leqslant l < 42$	6

A
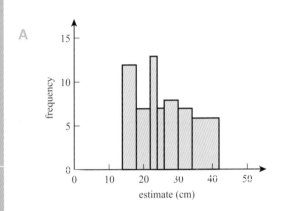

B
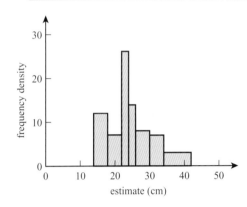

C
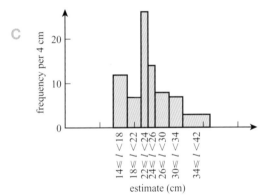

D
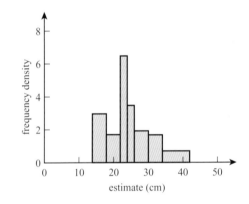

2 The following table shows the ages of a sample of the customers of a shop.

Age	13–16	17–19	20–25	26–35	36–55	56–70
Frequency	8	15	19	17	15	5

Between what limits should the next to last bar in the histogram be drawn?

A 35 to 55   B 36 to 56   C 35.5 to 55.5   D 35 to 56   E 36 to 55

3 The histogram shows the pulse rates in bpm (beats per minute) of a sample of people. How many people were in the sample?

A 7   B 29.5
C 30   D 40
E 200

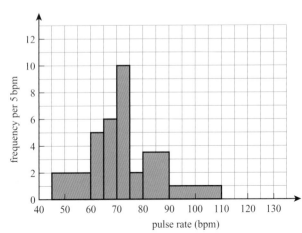

Exam-Style Question ⅅ⅃

A class of students are told to close their eyes; they are told to put up a hand when they think a minute has gone by. The times they take to put up their hands are summarised in the table.

i)   Draw a histogram to illustrate the data.

ii) Calculate an estimate of the median of the data.

Time (x seconds)	Number of students
$20 \leqslant x < 30$	2
$30 \leqslant x < 40$	4
$40 \leqslant x < 45$	3
$45 \leqslant x < 50$	6
$50 \leqslant x < 60$	7
$60 \leqslant x < 70$	6
$70 \leqslant x < 100$	2

Cumulative frequency curves and box-and-whisker plots

A ABOUT THIS TOPIC

Cumulative frequency curves are often used to estimate the median, quartiles and percentiles of grouped data; these measures are used to compare individuals or groups of people. For example, growth curves for babies and young children use them. Box-and-whisker diagrams provide a visual way of comparing sets of data. You are likely to come across these techniques elsewhere so it will be useful if you gain a good understanding of them.

R REMEMBER

- Frequency tables and rounding from GCSE.
- Median, cumulative frequency, measures of spread, outliers, stem-and-leaf diagrams and skewness from S1.

K KEY FACTS

- The median is the middle value of a set of data.
- To find the quartiles for a small data set, find the median first. Find the middle value of the values below the median for the lower quartile. Find the middle value of the values above the median for the upper quartile.
- Points on a cumulative frequency graph are plotted at the upper boundary of the group.
- To find the median from a cumulative frequency graph, read off the value with a cumulative frequency of $\frac{1}{2}n$, where n is the total number of data values.
- The upper and lower quartiles have cumulative frequencies of $\frac{3}{4}n$ and $\frac{1}{4}n$, respectively.
- In a box-and-whisker plot, the box shows the distance between the quartiles, the whiskers show the spread of the rest of the data.
- The interquartile range (IQR) is a measure of spread. IQR = upper quartile − lower quartile.
- A data value may be considered to be an outlier if it is more than $1.5 \times IQR$ above the upper quartile, or more than $1.5 \times IQR$ below the lower quartile.

Quartiles for small data sets

EXAMPLE 1 Find the median and quartiles of this data set: 2 4 6 6 7 8 11

SOLUTION

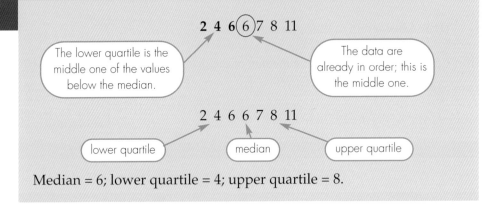

2 4 6 ⑥ 7 8 11

The lower quartile is the middle one of the values below the median.

The data are already in order; this is the middle one.

2 4 6 6 7 8 11

lower quartile   median   upper quartile

Median = 6; lower quartile = 4; upper quartile = 8.

With an even number of data items, the median will be between two values.

1 4 4 5 5 5 6 8

lower quartile   median   Upper quartile (the middle value of the data items above the median).

Median = 5; lower quartile = 4; upper quartile = 5.5.

Median and quartiles from a stem-and-leaf diagram

The data values in a stem-and-leaf diagram are in order.

EXAMPLE 2 The stem-and-leaf diagram below shows the ages of 21 office staff. Find the median and quartiles.

SOLUTION

```
1 | 8                    Key
2 | 1 5 6 6|7            2|1 means 21 years old
3 | 0 1 2 2 3 6 7 7
4 | 1 1|3 4 7
5 | 2
6 | 7
```

This is the median; there are 10 data items below it and 10 above it.

The positions of the lower and upper quartiles are shown by vertical blue lines.

The upper quartile is halfway between 41 and 43.

Median = 33; lower quartile = 26.5; upper quartile = 42.

Interquartile range (*IQR*)

- The interquartile range is a measure of spread. *IQR* = upper quartile – lower quartile.
- The interquartile range is easy to calculate and is not affected by extreme values.

EXAMPLE 3

Calculate the interquartile range for the data in example 2.

SOLUTION

$IQR = 42 - 26.5 = 15.5$

Outliers

A data item may be considered an outlier if it is more than $1.5 \times IQR$ above the upper quartile or more than $1.5 \times IQR$ below the lower quartile.

 You know another way of seeing whether a data item is an outlier using mean and standard deviation. Use the one that is easiest to work with in any situation but don't mix them up.

EXAMPLE 4

Could any of the ages in example 2 be regarded as outliers?

SOLUTION

$1.5 \times IQR = 1.5 \times 15.5 = 23.25$ ← You know what the quartiles are so it is easiest to use the method for outliers that uses quartiles.

$LQ - 23.25 = 26.5 - 23.25 = 3.25$
$UQ + 23.25 = 42 + 23.25 = 65.25$

Ages below 3.25 or above 65.25 years can be considered to be outliers so 67 is an outlier.

Box-and-whisker diagrams

The data from example 2 are shown in this box-and-whisker diagram.

The outlier is shown as a separate point.

Median

Lowest value

The upper whisker is at the highest value (not including the outlier).

LQ   UQ

There is an even horizontal axis for the age.

age (years)

Skewness in box-and-whisker plots

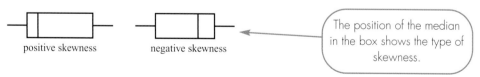

positive skewness   negative skewness

The position of the median in the box shows the type of skewness.

Cumulative frequency curves

EXAMPLE 5

The waiting time, in minutes, of a sample of customers at the post office is shown in the table. Draw a cumulative frequency diagram and find the median and interquartile range.

Time (t min)	Frequency
$0 < t \leq 1$	6
$1 < t \leq 2$	8
$2 < t \leq 3$	15
$3 < t \leq 4$	13
$4 < t \leq 5$	5
$5 < t \leq 6$	4
$6 < t \leq 7$	4
$7 < t \leq 10$	5

SOLUTION

First work out the cumulative frequencies.

Time (t min)	$t \leq 1$	$t \leq 2$	$t \leq 3$	$t \leq 4$	$t \leq 5$	$t \leq 6$	$t \leq 7$	$t \leq 10$
Cumulative freq	6	14	29	42	47	51	55	60

The vertical axis shows cumulative frequency.

To find the median, read across from the cumulative frequency that is half the total (60 ÷ 2 = 30).

To find the LQ, read across from the cumulative frequency that is one quarter of the total (60 ÷ 4 = 15).

The horizontal axis is an even scale showing the variable being studied.

Median = 3.1,
LQ = 2.1,
UQ = 4.6,
IQR = 4.6 − 2.1 = 2.5

A ADVICE

- The cumulative frequency is plotted at the upper boundary of each group. You may find it helpful to highlight these in your table (they are shown in blue above).
- Watch out for rounded data where there seem to be gaps between groups.

A ADVICE

Look carefully at the way the question is worded.
- If it asks for a cumulative frequency **curve**, then the points must be joined with a smooth curve.
- If it asks for a cumulative frequency **graph**, you can use either a smooth curve or straight lines to join the points.

Percentiles

The quartiles (including the median) divide the data into four equal groups.
Percentiles divide the data into 100 equal groups.

EXAMPLE 6   Find the 90th percentile of the data in example 5.

SOLUTION

90% of 60 is 54. ←   First find
the relevant percentage of
the cumulative frequency.

Reading from the cumulative frequency graph, the 90th percentile is 6.7.

  54 is not the 90th percentile. It tells you the cumulative frequency to look up from the graph.

 LINKS

Statistics   Cumulative distribution function (S3).

Test Yourself

1 The stem-and-leaf diagram on the right shows the hand widths of a sample of children.
Which box-and-whisker diagram correctly shows the same data?

8	6 6 6 7 7 7 8 8 8 8 8 9 9 9 9 9	Key
9*	0 1 1 1 1 2 2 3 4 4 4	9 | 5 means
9	5 5 6 7 8 9	9.5 cm
10*	2	

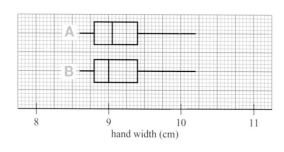

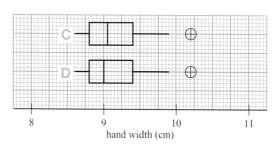

hand width (cm)   hand width (cm)

2 In a survey, people were asked how many portions of fruit and vegetables they ate the previous day. The cumulative frequency graph shows the ages of those who ate less than five portions. What kind of skewness do the data show? It may help to draw a box-and-whisker diagram.

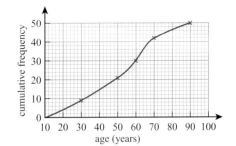

A Positive
B Negative
C None
D Not possible to tell

3 Which frequency table shows the data corresponding to the cumulative frequency curve in **question 2**?

A		B		C		D	
Age	**Frequency**	**Age**	**Frequency**	**Age**	**Frequency**	**Age**	**Frequency**
10–30	9	10–29	9	20–40	9	11–30	9
31–50	21	30–49	12	40–55	12	31–50	21
51–60	30	50–59	9	55–65	9	51–60	30
61–70	42	60–69	12	65–80	12	61–70	42
71–90	50	70–89	8	80–100	8	71–90	50

4 Here are five statements about the cumulative frequency curve in **question 2**. Four of them are false and one is true. Which one is true?
A The 90th percentile is 45.
B The youngest person must be 10 years old.
C There were 30 people aged less than 60.
D If you drew a histogram for the data, the second and fourth bars would be equal in height.
E The data have been grouped so you do not know what the exact ages of the people were. This makes it impossible to tell whether there were any outliers in this case.

Exam-Style Question ⊃L

As part of a biology experiment, a sample of leaves from a certain type of shrub is taken. The lengths of the leaves are measured. The results are summarised in the table.

i) Draw a cumulative frequency curve for the data.

ii) Estimate the median and the interquartile range.

iii) Showing your working, suggest the lengths of leaves that might be considered to be outliers.

Length (x cm)	Frequency
$2.0 \leqslant x < 3.0$	5
$3.0 \leqslant x < 4.0$	11
$4.0 \leqslant x < 4.5$	14
$4.5 \leqslant x < 5.0$	10
$5.0 \leqslant x < 6.0$	7
$6.0 \leqslant x < 8.0$	3

Probability

3

Probability and Venn diagrams

K KEY FACTS

- The probability of an event A can often be found using
  $$P(A) = \frac{\text{Number of ways } A \text{ can occur}}{\text{Total number of outcomes}}$$
  This only works if all outcomes are equally likely.
- $P(A') = 1 - P(A)$ where A' is the event '*not A*'.
- A probability of zero means an event cannot happen; a probability of 1 means it is certain to happen.
- Venn diagrams can be used to show either the number of outcomes or the probabilities of events.
- $P(A \cup B) = P(A) + P(B) - P(A \cap B)$ where $A \cup B$ is the *union of events* ('*A or B*') and $A \cap B$ is the *intersection of events* ('*A and B*').
- For mutually exclusive events, $P(A \cup B) = P(A) + P(B)$.

Finding probabilities using equally likely outcomes

You will almost certainly have used the following method to find probabilities:

$$P(A) = \frac{\text{Number of ways } A \text{ can occur}}{\text{Total number of outcomes}}$$

This only works if all outcomes are equally likely. It can be used in quite complicated situations, but you must be careful to count the equally likely outcomes correctly.

EXAMPLE 1

What is the probability of the spinner on the right landing on red, assuming that it is fair?

SOLUTION

All sections are equal so it is equally likely to land on any one of them.

Probability $= \frac{2}{4} = \frac{1}{2}$

EXAMPLE 2

What is the probability of the spinner on the left landing on red, assuming that it is fair?

SOLUTION

The sections are not all equal but you can put in some imaginary lines (see right) to get equal sections.

Probability $= \frac{2}{6} = \frac{1}{3}$

A ADVICE

You could also do this question by looking at the fraction of the total area that is coloured red. There is sometimes more than one correct way to approach a probability question; practice will help you find the ways that you prefer.

EXAMPLE 3

The types of students starting on a university course are shown in the table. One of the students who came from a college is selected at random. What is the probability that the student is female?

	Female	Male
11–18 school	43	80
College	17	98

SOLUTION

There are 17 + 98 = 115 students who came from a college, 17 of these are female.

Probability $= \frac{17}{115} \approx 0.148$

A ADVICE

Give answers to probability questions as fractions or decimals.

Impossible or certain events

- If an event cannot happen, its probability is 0.
- If an event is bound to happen, its probability is 1.

The probability that an event does not happen

Either an event happens or it does not.
$P(A') = 1 - P(A)$ where A' is the event 'not A'.

EXAMPLE 4

The weather forecast estimates the probability that it will rain tomorrow as $\frac{1}{4}$. What is the probability that it will not rain?

SOLUTION

$P(\text{no rain}) = 1 - \frac{1}{4} = \frac{3}{4}$

Using Venn diagrams

Venn diagrams are useful for showing the relationship between two or more events. They can be very helpful for finding probabilities.

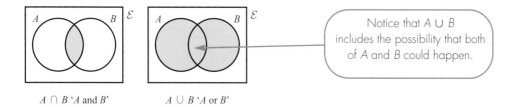

$A \cap B$ 'A and B' $A \cup B$ 'A or B'

Notice that $A \cup B$ includes the possibility that both of A and B could happen.

Venn diagrams for probability

EXAMPLE 5

The probability that it rains on a given day is 0.7, the probability that it rains and the bus is late is 0.4. The probability that it is not raining and the bus is not late is 0.1. What is the probability that the bus is late?

A ADVICE

It is easiest to start from the middle when filling in Venn diagrams.

SOLUTION

Let R denote the event that it rains, B denote the event that the bus is late.

1 First fill in the probability of both events, in the middle region.

2 The probability that neither event occurs is 0.1.

3 The probability in this region needs to add to the 0.4 in the middle to give 0.7.

4 All the probabilities need to add up to 1 so the probability for this region is 0.2.

5 P(bus late) = 0.4 + 0.2 = 0.6

The formula $P(A \cup B) = P(A) + P(B) - P(A \cap B)$ can be useful for some questions.

Venn diagrams can also be used for showing the number of outcomes, or the numbers in particular sets.

Venn diagrams for number of objects

EXAMPLE 6

There are 21 cars in a showroom; 13 of them are silver. Four of the silver cars are worth over £10 000. Two of the cars are neither silver nor worth over £10 000. One of the cars in the showroom is chosen at random as a prize in a competition. What is the probability that it is worth over £10 000?

SOLUTION

Let S denote the set of silver cars, V denote the set of cars worth over £10 000.

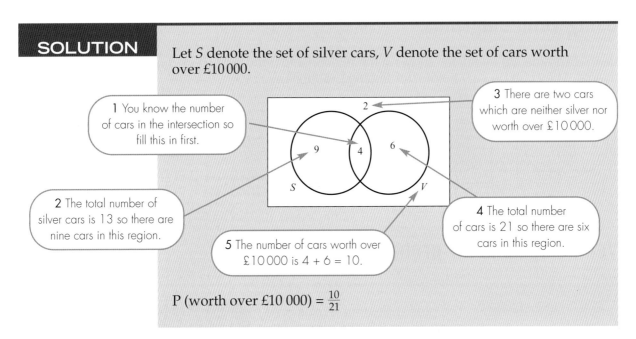

1 You know the number of cars in the intersection so fill this in first.

3 There are two cars which are neither silver nor worth over £10 000.

2 The total number of silver cars is 13 so there are nine cars in this region.

4 The total number of cars is 21 so there are six cars in this region.

5 The number of cars worth over £10 000 is 4 + 6 = 10.

$$\text{P (worth over £10 000)} = \frac{10}{21}$$

Mutually exclusive events

Mutually exclusive events cannot happen together.
A Venn diagram for two mutually exclusive events is shown here.

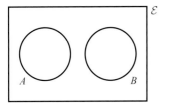

⚠ Be careful not to add probabilities automatically when you want the probability of one event or another event; this only works when they are mutually exclusive.

For mutually exclusive events,
$P(A \cup B) = P(A) + P(B)$.

EXAMPLE 7

A and B are two events with $P(A) = 0.7$ and $P(B) = 0.6$.
Explain why $P(A \cap B) \geq 0.3$.

SOLUTION

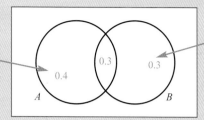

The total probability in the circle for A is 0.7.

The total probability in the circle for B is 0.6.

0.4   0.3   0.3

A   B

The overall total probability is 1.
If P(A ∩ B) = 0.3 then the probabilities are as shown in blue on the diagram and P(A ∪ B) = 1.
If P(A ∩ B) < 0.3 then P(A ∪ B) > 1 and this is not possible.
If P(A ∩ B) > 0.3 then P(A ∪ B) < 1 and this is possible.

LINKS

Statistics   Conditional probability (S1), Discrete random variables (S1), Combinations (S1).

Test Yourself ⊃L

1 Rosy and Jon are taking it in turns to throw a fair die with the numbers 1 to 6 on it. So far it has landed

6   1   4   6   2   2   2   4

Four of the following statements are false and one is true. Which is the true statement?

A The probability of it showing 2 on the next throw is $\frac{3}{8}$.
B It has not shown 5 yet so there is a high probability of getting 5 on the next throw.
C Getting three 2s in a row is very unlikely so there must be a typing error in the results.
D If they keep throwing the die, roughly one-sixth of the time the die will show 3.
E This die is more likely to land showing an even number than an odd number.

2 Raffle tickets numbered 277 to 575 inclusive are put into a large container and one ticket is taken out at random. What is the probability of a number divisible by 5 being chosen?

A $\frac{1}{5}$ B $\frac{30}{149}$ C $\frac{60}{299}$ D $\frac{59}{298}$ E $\frac{59}{299}$

3 For events A and B, P(A) = 0.4, P(A ∩ B) = 0.1, P(A' ∩ B') = 0.2. What is P(B)?
A −0.3   B 0.25   C 0.3   D 0.4   E 0.5

4 Some gardeners have phoned in to ask for their garden to appear on TV. The number of these gardens having certain features is shown in the Venn diagram. One of these gardens will be chosen at random to be in the TV show. What is the probability that a garden with both a vegetable patch and a pond will be chosen?

A $\frac{5}{34}$ B $\frac{13}{20}$ C $\frac{1}{8}$

D $\frac{3}{40}$ E $\frac{7}{20}$

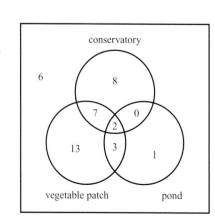

5 A box contains 50 chocolates. 20 of them are coated with dark chocolate, the rest with white chocolate. 28 of them are toffee-centred, the rest fudge. 12 of the dark chocolates have toffee centres. Alix chooses a chocolate at random. Four of the following statements are true and one is false. Which is the false statement?

A The probability of choosing one with a toffee centre and dark chocolate coating is 0.6.

B The probability of choosing one that does not have a dark chocolate coating is 0.6.

C The probability of choosing one with a toffee centre or a dark chocolate coating is 0.72.

D The probability of choosing one which does not have a toffee centre or a dark chocolate coating is 0.28.

E More than half of the white chocolates have toffee in them.

Exam-Style Question ⊃L

A and B are events with $P(A') = 0.3$, $P(B) = 0.5$ and $P(A \cup B) = 0.8$.

i)   Find $P(A)$.

ii)   Find $P(A \cap B)$.

iii) Draw a Venn diagram to show events A and B and mark on the probability for each region. Write down $P(A' \cap B')$.

iv)   Find $P(A \cap B')$.

v)   Are A and B mutually exclusive? Explain how you know.

Tree diagrams and sample space diagrams

A ABOUT THIS TOPIC

Sample space diagrams and tree diagrams are useful ways to organise your thinking about situations involving probability. You are likely to have come across them at GCSE, but make sure you can work with them correctly.

R REMEMBER

- Calculations with fractions and decimals from GCSE.
- Basic ideas of probability and mutually exclusive events from S1.

K KEY FACTS

- Sample space diagrams are used to display the outcomes when you have two trials happening together, each with equally likely outcomes.
- Tree diagrams can be used for working out the probability of two (or more) events.
- Once you have the correct probabilities on a tree diagram, you multiply along the branches to find the probability that all the relevant events happen.
- P(A happens at least once) = 1 − P(A never happens).

	H	T
H	HH	HT
T	TH	TT

Sample space diagrams

A sample space diagram is a table showing all the possible outcomes from two trials (or experiments), each of which has equally likely outcomes.

EXAMPLE 1

A fair spinner, with numbers 1 to 3 on it, is spun and an ordinary fair die is thrown. The two numbers are multiplied to give a score. What is the most likely score and what is the probability of getting it?

SOLUTION

Score		Number on die					
		1	2	3	4	5	6
Number on spinner	1	1	2	3	4	5	6
	2	2	4	6	8	10	12
	3	3	6	9	12	15	18

This cell in the sample space represents the event '2 on the spinner and 4 on the die'.

A ADVICE

If the question involves two numbers being multiplied or added then it makes your working easier to write the relevant results in the cells in the sample space.

The most frequently occurring score is 6 with a probability of $\frac{3}{18} = \frac{1}{6}$.

Sample space diagrams do not need to involve numbers.

EXAMPLE 2

Chris decides on his mid-morning snack by throwing a fair die which he has relabelled with 'apple', 'banana', 'cake', 'crisps', 'chocolate', 'raisins'. He then tosses a fair coin and only eats the snack if it lands heads. What is the probability that he eats cake, crisps or chocolate?

SOLUTION

	apple	banana	cake	crisps	chocolate	raisins
Heads (eats)			✓	✓	✓	
Tails (does not eat)						

Probability of eating cake, crisps or chocolate = $\frac{3}{12} = \frac{1}{4}$.

> Each cell in the sample space represents an equally likely outcome; you do not need to write anything in the cells.

Tree diagrams

Tree diagrams are useful for showing the possible things that can happen and also for working out probabilities of two (or more) events.

EXAMPLE 3

A box contains three red beads and two gold beads. Apart from the colour, the beads are identical. A contestant on a game show is blindfolded. She pulls out a bead then puts it back. She then pulls out a second bead. She wins a prize if she pulls out exactly one gold bead. What is the probability that she wins a prize?

SOLUTION

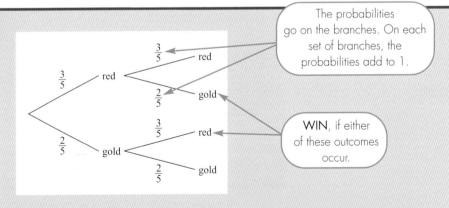

> The probabilities go on the branches. On each set of branches, the probabilities add to 1.

> WIN, if either of these outcomes occur.

P(win) = P(red, gold OR gold, red) = P(red, gold) + P(gold, red)

P(win) = $\frac{3}{5} \times \frac{2}{5} + \frac{2}{5} \times \frac{3}{5}$

$= \frac{6}{25} + \frac{6}{25} = \frac{12}{25}$

> Working along the branches, multiply the probabilities to find the probability that both gold and red occur.

 P(A or B) is not always the same as P(A) + P(B). This works if the events are mutually exclusive. There is more about mutually exclusive events in the previous section.

Tree diagrams and conditional probability

Sometimes additional information changes the probability. That is, the probability is conditional.

> ⚠ P(A and B) is not always the same as P(A) × P(B). They are only equal if the events are independent, as in example 3. In example 4, the probabilities on the branches vary depending on what has happened before. There is more about conditional probability in the next section.

EXAMPLE 4

The rules in the game in example 3 are changed slightly so that the first bead is not put back. What is the probability of getting exactly one gold bead now?

SOLUTION

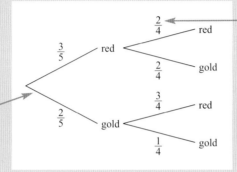

> If a red bead is chosen on the first go, there are 4 beads left and 2 of them are red.

> The probabilities on the first pair of branches are the same as in example 3.

$P(\text{win}) = P(\text{red, gold OR gold, red}) = P(\text{red, gold}) + P(\text{gold, red})$

$P(\text{win}) = \frac{3}{5} \times \frac{2}{4} + \frac{2}{5} \times \frac{3}{4}$

$= \frac{6}{20} + \frac{6}{20} = \frac{12}{20} = \frac{3}{5}$

> Working along the branches, multiply the probabilities to find the probability that both gold and red occur.

A ADVICE

- Do not cancel probabilities on tree diagrams. If you do, you could go wrong if the probabilities change for later branches.
- Always draw a tree diagram if the probabilities change, as in example 4. Drawing a tree diagram will often help you to get the correct probabilities.

A tree diagram can be as big as you need it to be.

EXAMPLE 5

My calculator gives me a random number with 3 decimal places. Assuming that each digit is equally likely to be from 0 to 9 inclusive, what is the probability that a random number contains at least one digit 7?

SOLUTION

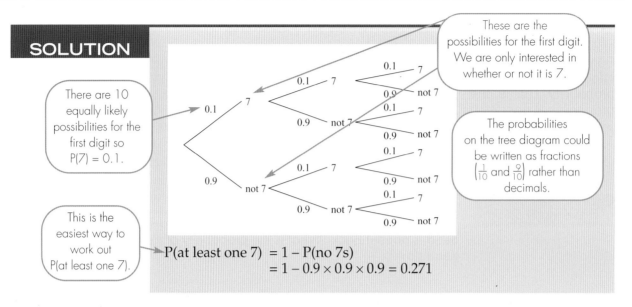

There are 10 equally likely possibilities for the first digit so P(7) = 0.1.

These are the possibilities for the first digit. We are only interested in whether or not it is 7.

The probabilities on the tree diagram could be written as fractions $\left(\frac{1}{10} \text{ and } \frac{9}{10}\right)$ rather than decimals.

This is the easiest way to work out P(at least one 7).

$$P(\text{at least one } 7) = 1 - P(\text{no } 7\text{s})$$
$$= 1 - 0.9 \times 0.9 \times 0.9 = 0.271$$

LINKS

Statistics   Conditional probability (S1), Combinations (S1), Binomial distribution (S1).

Test Yourself

1 A fair six-sided die is numbered 1, 1, 2, 2, 2, 3 and another fair six-sided die is numbered 1, 2, 3, 3, 5, 6. The two dice are thrown and the difference (larger − smaller) of the numbers they land on is found. What is the probability of a difference of 2?

   A $\frac{1}{5}$ B $\frac{1}{12}$ C $\frac{5}{36}$ ∘ D $\frac{1}{6}$ E $\frac{7}{36}$

2 An unbiased coin is tossed twice. What is the probability of getting one head and one tail?

   A $\frac{1}{3}$ B $\frac{1}{4}$ • C $\frac{1}{2}$ D 1   E 0

3 A jar contains 6 white discs and 4 black discs. A disc is taken out at random and replaced then the process is repeated. What is the probability of getting a black disc at least once?

   A $\frac{12}{25}$ ∘ B $\frac{16}{25}$ C $\frac{2}{3}$ D $\frac{3}{4}$ E $\frac{2}{5}$

4 A box of chocolates contains 12 chocolates. Ten of them are milk chocolates and two dark chocolates. Marsha takes two chocolates at random and eats them. What is the probability that she eats two milk chocolates?

   A $\frac{25}{36}$ B $\frac{2}{3}$ C $\frac{109}{66}$ ∘ D $\frac{15}{22}$ E $\frac{1}{4}$

5 Barry Mitchell is a footballer who has a 0.75 chance of scoring a goal from a penalty. He takes three penalties. Assume that the reults of these are independent of each other. Four of the statements below are false and one is true. Which is the true statement?

   A The probability that he scores exactly one goal is $\frac{3}{64}$.

   B The most likely number of goals he will score is 2.

   C The probability that he misses them all is 0.25 × 3 = 0.75.

   D He is more likely to score one goal than he is to miss at least two.

   E There is a better than even chance that he misses at least once.

SOLUTION

You can find P(A ∩ B) using the conditional probability formula.

$$P(A\mid B)=\frac{P(A\cap B)}{P(B)}$$

Put the probabilities you know into the formula.

$$0.8=\frac{P(A\cap B)}{0.5}$$

$$P(A\cap B)=0.8\times0.5=0.4$$

A ADVICE

Notice that the formula for $P(A\mid B)=\dfrac{P(A\cap B)}{P(B)}$ has $P(B)$ in the denominator.

EXAMPLE 3

P(A) = 0.6, P(B) = 0.5, P(A ∩ B) = 0.4. Work out P(A ∪ B).

SOLUTION

You can put the probabilities into a Venn diagram.

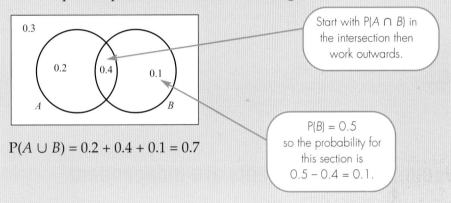

Start with P(A ∩ B) in the intersection then work outwards.

$$P(A\cup B)=0.2+0.4+0.1=0.7$$

P(B) = 0.5 so the probability for this section is 0.5 − 0.4 = 0.1.

A ADVICE

- You could use the formula P(A ∪ B) = P(A) + P(B) − P(A ∩ B) without drawing a Venn diagram.
- P(A | B) does not appear in the Venn diagram but it could be worked out using

$$P(A\mid B)=\frac{P(A\cap B)}{P(B)}=\frac{0.4}{0.5}=\frac{4}{5}.$$

- Notice that $P(B\mid A)=\dfrac{P(A\cap B)}{P(A)}=\dfrac{0.4}{0.6}=\dfrac{2}{3}$ and this is different to P(A | B).

Conditional probability and tree diagrams

The idea of putting conditional probabilities on the branches of tree diagrams has been covered in the previous section (see example 4 on page 49).

Tree diagrams can also be used in working out other conditional probabilities.

EXAMPLE 4

Nathan can drive home on either road X or road Y. Road X has more traffic jams on it but is quicker if there is no traffic jam. He flips a coin to decide which road to take. The probability of a traffic jam on road X is $\frac{2}{3}$ and the probability of a traffic jam on road Y is $\frac{1}{6}$. Nathan rings home to say that he is in a traffic jam. What is the probability that he is on road X?

SOLUTION

You want $P(X \mid jam)$ so write down the conditional probability formula:

$$P(X \mid jam) = \frac{P(X \cap jam)}{P(jam)}$$

You can put the information about probabilities in a tree diagram. Now use the tree diagram to work out the probabilities in the formula.

(X, jam)
or
(Y, jam)

$P(X \cap jam) = \frac{1}{2} \times \frac{2}{3} = \frac{1}{3}$

$P(jam) = \frac{1}{2} \times \frac{2}{3} + \frac{1}{2} \times \frac{1}{6} = \frac{5}{12}$

so $P(X \mid jam) = \frac{1}{3} \div \frac{5}{12} = \frac{1}{3} \times \frac{12}{5} = \frac{4}{5}$

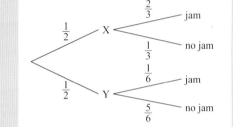

⚠ Be careful to get the conditional probability the right way round. In example 4, we know he is in a jam and want the probability he is on road X.

Deciding whether events are independent

EXAMPLE 5

A random sample of 200 plants of a particular variety of flower were examined. For these plants, *A* is the event 'plant has dark leaves' and *B* is the event 'plant has red flowers'. The Venn diagram shows the numbers of plants with these characteristics. Find:

i) P(*A*)
ii) P(*B*)
iii) P(*A* ∩ *B*)
iv) State whether events *A* and *B* are independent, giving reasons for your decision.

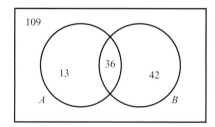

SOLUTION

i) $P(A) = \frac{13 + 36}{200} = 0.245$

There are 200 plants altogether.

ii) $P(B) = \frac{36 + 42}{200} = 0.39$

iii) $P(A \cap B) = \frac{36}{200} = 0.18$

iv) If the events are independent then $P(A \cap B) = P(A) \times P(B)$.
$P(A) \times P(B) = 0.245 \times 0.39 = 0.09555$ but $P(A \cap B) = 0.18$.

These are not equal so the events are not independent.

Be careful not to assume that
$P(A \cap B)$ is $P(A) \times P(B)$. You
can work out $P(A \cap B)$ directly
from the Venn diagram in
example 5.

A ADVICE

If you are asked to explain whether two events
are independent you are not expected to write a
paragraph about why they should not affect the
probability of each other happening. You should
use one of the facts that, for independent events,
$P(B \mid A) = P(B)$ or $P(A \cap B) = P(A)P(B)$, explaining
briefly what you are doing, as in example 5.

 LINKS

Statistics   Hypothesis testing (S1 and beyond).

Test Yourself ⟩L

1 A jar contains 8 red discs and 5 green discs. Two discs are picked at random. What
   is the probability that the second disc is red, given that the first disc is green?

   A $\frac{1}{2}$ B $\frac{2}{3}$ C $\frac{7}{12}$ D $\frac{8}{13}$

   E It is impossible to work out without more information.

2 A researcher is conducting a survey by asking questions in the street. She keeps a record
   of the number of people who were willing to answer her questions and of those who
   were not. The results are shown in the table. Assuming that these results are typical, what
   is the probability that someone is willing to answer given that the person is female?

   A $\frac{81}{263}$ B $\frac{132}{263}$

   C $\frac{142}{263}$ D $\frac{81}{132}$

   E $\frac{81}{142}$

	Male	Female
Willing to answer	51	81
Not willing to answer	70	61

3 A fair coin is tossed. If it lands heads, a ball is chosen at random from jar X. If it lands
   tails, a ball is chosen at random from jar Y. There are 6 green balls and 5 blue balls in
   jar X. There are 2 green balls and 8 blue balls in jar Y. Four of the following statements
   are true and one is false. Which is the false statement?

   A The probability of choosing a green ball is $\frac{41}{110}$.

   B The events 'the coin lands tails' and 'a green ball is chosen' are independent
      because the balls cannot know how the coin has landed.

   C Given that a green ball is chosen, the probability that the coin landed tails is $\frac{11}{41}$.

   D The probability of choosing a green ball given that the coin lands heads is $\frac{6}{11}$.

   E A blue ball is more likely to be chosen than a green ball.

4 $P(A) = 0.5$, $P(B) = 0.4$, $P(B \mid A) = 0.3$. What is $P(A \cup B)$?

   A 0.15   B 0.2   C 0.7   • D 0.75   E 0.9

5 Munchy Biscuits are sold in cartons. During a promotion, the lids of the
   cartons are coloured and numbered on the inside. Customers win if the
   lid is red with number 10. 30% of the lids are red. 20% of the lids
   have a number 10. For the red lids, 10% of them are numbered 10.
   What is the probability of winning?

   A 0.5   B 0.1   C 0.06   ◦ D 0.03   E 0.02

Exam-Style Question ⊃L

Bill's cat has 8 kittens: 3 female and 5 male. Alex is going to have two of them. Two of them are selected at random for Alex.

i)   What is the probability that two females are selected?

ii) What is the probability that one of each gender is selected?

iii) What is the probability that two females are selected given that both kittens chosen are of the same gender?

Discrete random variables

4

Discrete random variables

A ABOUT THIS TOPIC

A variable can take different values. A discrete random variable can only take discrete values. Examples of discrete random variables include the score on a die, the proportion of heads when tossing four coins, the number of children in a family. The probability distribution gives the probability of each possible value. The ideas in this section are general and apply to both theoretical and real-life situations.

R REMEMBER

- Substituting into formulae from GCSE and C1.
- Types of data, vertical line charts and probability from S1.

K KEY FACTS

- Upper case (capital) letters are used to stand for discrete random variables. For example, S stands for 'the total score when two dice are thrown'.
- Lower case letters are used to stand for values of the discrete random variable. So, in this example $s = 2, 3, 4, \ldots, 12$.
- Each possible value of the random variable has a probability of occurring which is between 0 and 1.
- If the random variable X can take values $r_1, r_2, r_3, \ldots, r_n$ with probabilities $p_1, p_2, p_3, \ldots, p_n$ respectively then $\sum_{i=1}^{n} p_i = 1$. That is, all the probabilities add up to 1.
- A discrete probability distribution can be illustrated by a vertical line chart.

Discrete random variables

Discrete random variables can only take discrete values. Each possible value has a probability of occurring.

EXAMPLE 1   A fair coin is tossed twice. Fill in the probability of each possible number of heads.

Number of heads	0	1	2
Probability			

The probabilities can be found by drawing a sample space diagram (shown here). Use these values to complete the table.

Number of heads		First toss	
		H	T
Second toss	H	2	1
	T	1	0

Number of heads	0	1	2
Probability	$\frac{1}{4}$	$\frac{1}{2}$	$\frac{1}{4}$

There are 4 items in the sample space, one of them is '0 heads'.

The probability distribution of a discrete random variable

The probability distribution can be a table which gives a probability for each value (as in example 1) or it can be a formula which gives a probability for each value (as in the following example 2).

EXAMPLE 2

The random variable X can take values 1, 2, 3, 4. The probability of each possible value is given by $P(X = r) = \dfrac{5}{4r(r + 1)}$. Find $P(X = 2)$.

SOLUTION

$$P(X = 2) = \frac{5}{4 \times 2 \times 3} = \frac{5}{24}$$

Put 2 in the formula in place of r.

R RULE

- For each possible value of the random variable, its probability is between 0 and 1.
- If the random variable X can take values r_1, r_2, r_3, ..., r_n with probabilities p_1, p_2, p_3, ..., p_n respectively then $\sum\limits_{i=1}^{n} p_i = 1$. That is, all the probabilities add up to 1.

EXAMPLE 3

The random variable X has a probability distribution given by the formula $P(X = r) = k(7 - 2r)$ for $r = 1, 2, 3$. k is a constant. Find the value of k.

SOLUTION

r	1	2	3
$P(X = r)$	$5k$	$3k$	k

Start by putting the values of r into the formula and writing the probabilities in a table.

The probabilities add up to 1 so $5k + 3k + k = 1$

$$9k = 1$$
$$k = \tfrac{1}{9}.$$

Illustrating discrete random variables

A vertical line chart is a good way to illustrate the probability distribution of a discrete random variable.

EXAMPLE 4 Illustrate the probability distribution in example 3.

SOLUTION

r	1	2	3
$P(X = r)$	$\frac{5}{9}$	$\frac{3}{9}$	$\frac{1}{9}$

Use the value of k you worked out to write the probabilities in a table.

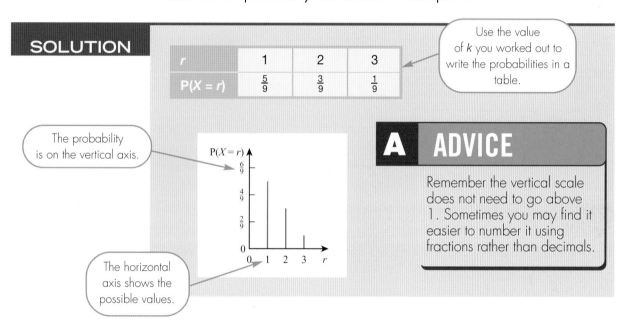

The probability is on the vertical axis.

The horizontal axis shows the possible values.

Working with discrete random variables

You can use the probabilities for discrete random variables in all the usual ways. Different formulae can be used for the probabilities for different values.

EXAMPLE 5 The probability distribution of the random variable X is given by

$P(X = r) = 0.2 \times 0.8^{r-1}$ for r = 1, 2, 3, 4, 5
$P(X = r) = k$ for r = 6 (k is a constant)
$P(X = r) = 0$ otherwise.

i) Find the value of k.
ii) Two independent values of X are generated, one after the other. Find the probability that their total is greater than 10.

This is just a way of saying that values of r which are not 1, 2, 3, 4, 5, 6 cannot happen.

SOLUTION

i) Using the formula $P(X = r) = 0.2 \times 0.8^{r-1}$, for values of r from 1 to 5, gives the probabilities in this table.

r	1	2	3	4	5	6
$P(X = r)$	0.2	0.16	0.128	0.1024	0.08192	k

$0.2 + 0.16 + 0.128 + 0.1024 + 0.08192 + k = 1$
$0.67232 + k = 1$
so $k = 0.32768$

> All the probabilities add up to 1.

> The probability for 6 is just k.

ii) A total greater than 10 can come from these pairs of values: (5, 6) or (6, 5) or (6, 6).
$P(\text{total} > 10) = P(5, 6) + P(6, 5) + P(6, 6)$
$P(\text{total} > 10) = 0.08192 \times 0.32768 + 0.32768 \times 0.08192 + 0.32768 \times 0.32768 \approx 0.161$

A ADVICE

You could draw a tree diagram for part **ii)** using the probabilities from part **i)** and you should do so if it will help you to see how to work it out.

Modelling with discrete random variables

Theoretical probability distributions are used as approximations to real-life situations so that predictions can be made about what is likely to happen.

EXAMPLE 6

The number of people travelling in a car, X, is modelled by the probability distribution $P(X = r) = k \times 0.4^r$ for $r = 1, 2, 3, 4$ (k is a constant). Find the value of k. Hence find the proportion of cars which only have one person travelling in them.

SOLUTION

r	1	2	3	4
$P(X = r)$	$0.4k$	$0.16k$	$0.064k$	$0.0256k$

> Start by putting the values of r into the formula and writing the probabilities in a table.

$0.4k + 0.16k + 0.064k + 0.0256k = 1$
$0.6496k = 1$
$k = 1 \div 0.6496 = 1.54 \text{ (3 s.f.)}$
$P(X = 1) = 0.4k \approx 0.4 \times 1.54 = 0.616$

> Remember all the probabilities add up to 1.

About 62% of cars only have one person in them.

> The final answer can be left as a decimal or given as a percentage but it makes sense to round it as the value of k was not exact.

LINKS

Statistics   Binomial distribution (S1), Poisson distribution (S2), Continuous random variables (S3), Probability generating functions (S4).

Test Yourself ⊃L

1 Which one of the five options in this question could be the probability distribution of a discrete random variable?

A

r	0	1	2	3
P(X = r)	0.56	k	0.24	0.21

B $P(X = r) = k(r + 1)$ for $r = 0, 1, 2$
  $P(X = r) = kr^2$ for $r = 4, 5$
  $P(X = r) = 0$ otherwise

C $P(X = r) = k(r^2 - 2r)$ for $r = 1, 2, 3$

D

r	2	3	4	5
P(X = r)	0.36	0.18	0.23	0.21

E $P(X = r) = \dfrac{kr}{r + 1}$ for all values of r between 1 and 5 (inclusive), i.e. $1 \leqslant r \leqslant 5$

2 A discrete random variable, X, has the probability distribution

  $P(X = r) = k(2r^2 - r)$ for $r = 1, 2, 3$
  $P(X = r) = 3k$ for $r = 4$
  $P(X = r) = 0$ otherwise.

Find the value of k.

A 25   B $\dfrac{1}{22}$ C $\dfrac{1}{54}$ D 1   E 0.04

3 A discrete random variable, X, has the probability distribution shown in the table.

r	0	1	2	3	4
P(X = r)	0.25	0.2	0.15	0.3	0.1

Find $P(1 \leqslant X < 3)$.
A 0.15   B 0.35   C 0.45   D 0.55   E 0.65

4 X = the larger score when two fair dice are thrown. Which one of the following is the correct probability distribution for X?

A $P(X = r) = \dfrac{2r - 1}{36}$ for $r = 1, 2, 3, 4, 5, 6$

B $P(X = r) = \dfrac{1}{6}$ for $r = 1, 2, 3, 4, 5, 6$ $P(X = r) = \dfrac{1}{6}$ for $r = 1, 2, 3, 4,$

C $P(X = r) = \dfrac{2r + 1}{36}$ for $r = 1, 2, 3, 4, 5, 6$

D $P(X = r) = \dfrac{r}{21}$ for $r = 1, 2, 3, 4, 5, 6$

E $P(X = r) = \dfrac{r - 1}{15}$ for $r = 1, 2, 3, 4, 5, 6$

Exam-Style Question ⊃L

Five girls each buy a gift. The gifts are collected together and they each choose one at random. The probability distribution for the number of girls, X, who end up with the gift they originally bought is shown in the table.

r	0	1	2	3	4	5
$P(X = r)$	p	$\frac{3}{8}$	$\frac{1}{6}$	$\frac{1}{12}$	0	$\frac{1}{120}$

i)   Find the value of p.

ii)   Explain why it is impossible for X to be 4.

iii)   Show that $P(X = 5) = \frac{1}{120}$.

iv)   Illustrate the probability distribution with a suitable diagram.

Expectation and variance of a discrete random variable

A ABOUT THIS TOPIC

The expectation is the mean of a random variable. Expectation and variance of a discrete random variable are worked out from probabilities, rather than from data values, so they refer to the whole population rather than a particular sample. Understanding this topic will extend your understanding of measures of location and spread.

R REMEMBER

- Mean and variance from a frequency table from S1.
- Discrete random variables from S1.

K KEY FACTS

- The expectation of the random variable X is denoted by $E(X)$; the symbol μ is often used to stand for the expectation. It is sometimes called 'the expected value'.
- $E(X) = \mu = \sum r\, P(X = r)$
  That is, multiply each value by its probability and add the results.
- The variance of X is denoted by $Var(X)$; the symbol σ^2 is often used to stand for the variance, with σ for the standard deviation.
- $Var(X) = \sigma^2 = E(X^2) - [E(X)]^2$
  $\qquad\quad = \sum r^2 P(X = r) - \mu^2$
- Standard deviation $= \sigma = \sqrt{Var(X)}$

Expectation

The expectation is the population mean, or 'long run' mean. The calculation is similar to calculating the mean from a frequency table.

R RULE

- To find the expectation, multiply each value by its probability and add the results.
- $E(X) = \mu = \sum r\, P(X = r)$

EXAMPLE 1

A charity lottery offers prizes of £10, £100 or £1000. The probabilities of winning are shown in the table.

Winnings (£)	0	10	100	1000
Probability	$\frac{1987}{2000}$	$\frac{1}{200}$	$\frac{1}{1000}$	$\frac{1}{2000}$

i) What is the expectation of the winnings?
ii) The committee organising the lottery need to decide a price at which to sell the tickets. Carlotta suggests selling them at £1 but Mike says they will sell more tickets if they sell them at 50p each. Which is the better price for the tickets? Explain your answer.

SOLUTION

i) $\text{Expectation} = 0 \times \frac{1987}{2000} + 10 \times \frac{1}{200} + 100 \times \frac{1}{1000} + 1000 \times \frac{1}{2000}$

$= 0 + \frac{10}{200} + \frac{100}{1000} + \frac{1000}{2000} = \frac{13}{20} = 0.65$

The expected win is £0.65.

> The expectation is an average value. The winnings were in pounds so it makes sense to give the answer as a decimal; the final answer should have units on it.

ii) On average each ticket pays out 65p so the selling price needs to be more than this, otherwise they will make a loss. £1 is the better selling price.

 Remember that the expectation is a mean. In everyday speech, we use the word 'expected' to mean something that is likely to happen. The expectation of a random variable may not be likely to happen. For instance, in example 1 the expected win is £0.65 but you could not win this amount.

Variance

The variance is a measure of spread.

R RULE

$\mathrm{Var}(X) = \sigma^2 = E(X^2) - [E(X)]^2$

$= \sum r^2\, P(X = r) - \mu^2$

A ADVICE

- Even if you are not asked to work out the expectation, you will need to work it out to be able to find the variance.
- It is easiest to set your working out if you have the probabilities in a table. Write them in a table even if you are given them as a formula.

EXAMPLE 2

The probability distribution for the random variable X is given by

$$P(X = r) = \frac{(5-r)^2}{30} \quad \text{for } r = 1, 2, 3, 4$$

$$P(X = r) = 0 \quad \text{otherwise}.$$

> This just means other values cannot occur.

Find the expectation and variance of X.

SOLUTION

r	1	2	3	4
$P(X = r)$	$\frac{16}{30}$	$\frac{9}{30}$	$\frac{4}{30}$	$\frac{1}{30}$

> Start by putting the values of r into the formula and writing the probabilities in a table.

A ADVICE

You do not need to include any values with a probability of zero in the table.

$$E(X) = 1 \times \tfrac{16}{30} + 2 \times \tfrac{9}{30} + 3 \times \tfrac{4}{30} + 4 \times \tfrac{1}{30}$$

$$= \tfrac{16}{30} + \tfrac{18}{30} + \tfrac{12}{30} + \tfrac{4}{30} = \tfrac{5}{3}$$

> Multiply each value by its probability and add to find the expectation.

$$E(X^2) = 1^2 \times \tfrac{16}{30} + 2^2 \times \tfrac{9}{30} + 3^2 \times \tfrac{4}{30} + 4^2 \times \tfrac{1}{30}$$

$$= \tfrac{16}{30} + \tfrac{36}{30} + \tfrac{36}{30} + \tfrac{16}{30} = \tfrac{104}{30} = \tfrac{52}{15}$$

> Start the calculation for the variance by working out $E(X^2)$: square each possible value of X, multiply by its probability and add.

> Complete the working for the variance by subtracting the square of the mean from $E(X^2)$.

$$\text{Var}(X) = E(X^2) - [E(X)]^2$$

$$= \tfrac{52}{15} - \left(\tfrac{5}{3}\right)^2 = \tfrac{52}{15} - \tfrac{25}{9} = \tfrac{156}{45} - \tfrac{125}{45} = \tfrac{31}{45}$$

- $E(X^2)$ is not the final answer when you are working out variance. It is part of your working.
- You need to use the expectation when working out the variance. Even if you round the expectation, you should still use the unrounded value when working out the variance so make sure you write down the exact value or store it in your calculator memory.

A ADVICE

- Variance must be positive so if you get a negative answer you know it is wrong.
- There is a lot of working in finding the variance. In an exam, if you think your final answer is wrong, don't spend a long time looking for the mistake. You will probably get most of the marks for the working, if you have shown it clearly. Your time will be better spent doing another question.
- If you are asked to work out the standard deviation, you should work out the variance first then find its square root to get the standard deviation.

Using expectation and variance

Many questions about discrete random variables will require you to use a combination of techniques to get the answer.

EXAMPLE 3

The random variable X is the number of people living in a house. X has the probability distribution shown in the table.

r	1	2	3	4	5	6	7	8
$P(X = r)$	0.298	0.345	0.153	0.136	0.048	0.016	0.003	0.001

You are given that $E(X) = \mu = 2.356$. Find the standard deviation, σ, and hence find $P(X > \mu + 2\sigma)$.

SOLUTION

Start the calculation for the variance by working out $E(X^2)$.

$$E(X^2) = 1^2 \times 0.298 + 2^2 \times 0.345 + 3^2 \times 0.153 + 4^2 \times 0.136 + 5^2 \times 0.048$$
$$+ 6^2 \times 0.016 + 7^2 \times 0.003 + 8^2 \times 0.001$$
$$= 7.218$$

$$\sigma^2 = \text{Var}(X) = E(X^2) - [E(X)]^2$$
$$= 7.218 - 2.356^2 = 1.667\,264$$

Remember to take the square root of the variance to get the standard deviation.

$$\sigma = \sqrt{1.667\,264} = 1.291 \text{ (3 d.p.)}$$

X could be 5 or 6 or 7 or 8.

$$\mu + 2\sigma = 2.356 + 2 \times 1.291 = 4.938$$

$$P(X > \mu + 2\sigma) = P(X > 4.938) = 0.048 + 0.016 + 0.003 + 0.001 = 0.068$$

LINKS

Statistics — Binomial distribution (S1), Poisson distribution (S2), Continuous random variables (S3), Probability generating functions (S4).

Decision — Expected monetary value (D2).

⚠ Values that are more than two standard deviations from the mean are often considered to be outliers. This does not mean they are errors; they can occur by chance.

Test Yourself

Questions 1 and 2 are about the random variable X, the number of heads on 5 tosses of a biased coin. In an experiment, a biased coin is tossed 5 times and the number of heads recorded. This is repeated a very large number of times, giving rise to this probability distribution:

r	0	1	2	3	4	5
$P(X = r)$	0.08	0.26	0.34	0.23	0.08	0.01

1 What is E(X)? (Rounded answers are given to 3 s.f.)

A 0.333   B 0.167   C 1   D 2   E 2.5

2 What is Var(X)? (Rounded answers are given to 3 s.f.)

A 1.22   B 3.22   C −3.52   D 4   E 5.22

3 Here are five statements about discrete random variables. One of them is true and the other four are false. Which is the true statement?

A $E(X^2) = [E(X)]^2$ for all discrete random variables, X.

B The possible values of a discrete random variable must be whole numbers.

C The possible values of a discrete random variable cannot be negative.

D The mean of the discrete random variable X is given by $\dfrac{\sum rP(X = r)}{n}$, where n is the number of possible values.

E Var(X) $\geqslant$ 0 for all discrete random variables, X.

4 A random variable, X, has probability distribution given by

$$P(X = r) = \frac{(r + 1)^2}{30} \quad \text{for } r = 0, 1, 2, 3.$$

What is the standard deviation of X? (Answers are rounded to 3 s.f.)

A 0.143   B 0.689   C 0.830   D 2.33   E 2.48

5 Daniel plays solitaire on his computer. He has a $\frac{1}{5}$ probability of winning each time he plays it. He likes to win but does not want to spend too long playing the game so he plays up to a maximum of 4 games in a session. He stops as soon as he wins a game, or if he has played 4 games and lost them all. What is the mean number of games he plays in a session?

A 0.8   B 1.3136   C 2.5   D 2.952   E 3

Exam-Style Question $\blacktriangleright$L

A statistician is investigating the number of children that women have. She models the number of children per woman, X, by the probability distribution

$P(X = r) = k(5 - r)(4 + r)$ for $r = 0, 1, 2, 3, 4$, where k is a constant.

i)   Find the value of k.

ii)   Find E(X) and Var(X).

iii) Another statistician says that some women have more than four children and that possible values of r should include 5 and 6. Would it be possible to use the same model, but with a different value of k? Explain your answer.

Further probability

5

Factorials, permutations and combinations

A ABOUT THIS TOPIC

Factorials, permutations and combinations are all connected with working out the number of choices or arrangements of a collection of objects. They have real-life applications; for example, working out how many different choices are possible in a lottery. Understanding this topic will help you to work out some probabilities more easily.

R REMEMBER

- Tree diagrams from S1.

K KEY FACTS

- The number of ways of arranging n unlike objects in line is $n!$
- $n! = n(n-1)(n-2) \ldots \times 3 \times 2 \times 1$
- $0! = 1$
- The number of permutations of r objects from n unlike objects is
  $${}^nP_r = \frac{n!}{(n-r)!} \quad \text{(order matters)}.$$
- The number of combinations of r objects from n unlike objects is
  $${}^nC_r = \binom{n}{r} = \frac{n!}{r!(n-r)!} \quad \text{(order does not matter)}.$$

Factorials

R RULE

- The number of ways of arranging n unlike objects in line is $n!$
- $n! = n(n-1)(n-2) \ldots \times 3 \times 2 \times 1$

This helps us to answer questions such as in the following example.

EXAMPLE 1   Three horses take part in a race. Their names are Arthur's Seat, Blessed Dawn and Cinderella. How many different ways can they finish?

SOLUTION

There are three horses. The number of different ways they can finish is $3! = 6$.

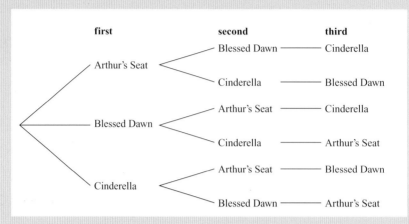

(You can see all six ways from a tree diagram; this one does not have the probabilities on it.)

There are three possibilities for the first place. For each of these, there are two possibilities for the second place and then only one for the third place. Hence the total number of orders is $3 \times 2 \times 1$.

A ADVICE

You can use the factorial button on your calculator to work out factorials but it is helpful if you also understand the principles of why the number of possibilities is calculated by multiplying.

Permutations

This way of thinking can be extended to situations where some (but not all) of the items are chosen and put in order.

EXAMPLE 2

There are eight horses in a race. Find the number of different ways that first, second and third places can be attained.

SOLUTION

There are eight possibilities for the first place. For each of these, there are seven possibilities for the second place and then six for the third place.

The number of possible orders is $8 \times 7 \times 6 = 336$.

This can be written as $\dfrac{8 \times 7 \times 6 \times 5 \times 4 \times 3 \times 2 \times 1}{5 \times 4 \times 3 \times 2 \times 1} = \dfrac{8!}{5!} = {}^8P_3$.

R RULE

The number of permutations of r objects from n unlike objects is ${}^nP_r = \dfrac{n!}{(n-r)!}$ (order matters).

A ADVICE

You should have a ${}^nP_r$ button on your calculator. Check that you can use it to get the answer to example 2 directly.

Combinations

Sometimes the order that items are chosen in is not important; the only thing that matters is which objects are chosen. The working in this situation is related to that above.

EXAMPLE 3

Jason has eight different books he wants to read. He will choose three at random to take on holiday. How many possible selections are there?

SOLUTION

If the order he chose them in mattered, there would be $^8P_3 = 336$ possible selections. Each set of three books could be chosen in six different orders (see example 1) so each selection has been counted six times. The number of selections is $\frac{336}{6} = 56$. This can be written $\frac{^8P_3}{3!} = {}^8C_3$.

R RULE

The number of combinations of r objects from n unlike objects is $^nC_r = \binom{n}{r} = \frac{n!}{r!(n-r)!}$ (order does not matter).

A ADVICE

You should have a ^nC_r button on your calculator. Check that you can use it to get the answer to example 3 directly.

In questions involving permutations and combinations, it is important to be clear about what you are working out and to set your working out clearly.

EXAMPLE 4

A type of four-digit number is made by choosing four random digits from 1, 2, 3, 4, 5, 6, 7, 8, 9. Digits cannot be repeated. How many different four-digit numbers of this type are there?

SOLUTION

The order of the digits matters so there are
$^9P_4 = \frac{9!}{(9-4)!} = \frac{9!}{5!} = 3024$ numbers.

A ADVICE

Sometimes you will be able to get the answer directly by using the appropriate button on your calculator but you should write down '$^9P_4$' as well as the answer, or whatever calculation you are doing, so that your method is clear.

EXAMPLE 5 How many of the four-digit numbers in example 4 are divisible by 5?

SOLUTION

For the number to be divisible by 5, the last digit has to be 5.

The first three digits can be chosen from 1, 2, 3, 4, 6, 7, 8, 9 and the order matters.

You can only choose the first three digits; the last digit must be 5.

There are $^8P_3 = \dfrac{8!}{(8-3)!} = \dfrac{8!}{5!} = 336$ possible numbers.

Finding probabilities

When you know how many ways there of doing something, you can use this information to help you find a probability.

EXAMPLE 6 One of the four-digit numbers from example 4 is chosen at random. What is the probability that it is divisible by 5?

SOLUTION

Number of four-digit numbers which are divisible by 5, worked out in example 5.

$$\dfrac{336}{3024} = \dfrac{1}{9}$$

Total number of possible four-digit numbers, worked out in example 4.

There is more about finding probabilities in the next section.

LINKS

Pure	Binomial expansions (C1, C4), Maclaurin series (FP2).
Statistics	Binomial distribution (S1).
Decision	Route inspection problem (D2).

Test Yourself ▶L

1 Ellie is making a list of the Christmas presents she wants. There are 9 items on her list. Her mother tells her she can only ask for 3 of them. How many different ways can she choose the final 3?

  A 6   B 9   C 84   D 504   E 362 880

2 When choosing their options, students in a college have 7 subjects to choose from. They each write down their first choice, second choice and third choice on their option forms. How many different possible lists of choices are there?

  A 6   B 7   C 35   D 210   E 840

3 John is playing a game on the computer. The computer puts 4 coloured pegs in a row in a random order but does not show the order. There is one blue, one green, one red and one yellow peg. John has to guess the order. What is the probability that he gets the order right on his first go?

  A 0   B 0.041$\dot{6}$ C 0.25   D 1
  E Not possible to work out

4 A fair die is thrown 4 times and the 4 values are written, one after the other, to make a 4-digit number. For example, scores 1, 2, 2, 3 would give the number 1223. How many different even numbers are possible?

   A 24   B 180   C 360   D 648   E 1296

5 A keypad for a lock has digits 0 to 9 and letters X, Y on it. It is possible to program security codes into it in different ways but digits cannot be used more than once in any code. Four of the following statements are false and one is true. Which is the true statement?

  A For codes consisting of 4 digits followed by a letter, with the digits needing to be keyed in the right order, the number of possible codes is 10080.

  B For codes consisting of 5 digits, which can be keyed in any order, the number of possible codes is 792.

  C For codes using digits only, there are more codes consisting of 6 digits (in any order) than there are codes consisting of 4 digits (in any order).

  D For codes consisting of 4 digits, chosen from 1 to 5, followed by a letter, with the digits needing to be keyed in the right order, the number of possible codes is 120.

  E An office uses a keypad like this. There is a new code each week. The code consists of 3 digits, which can be keyed in any order, followed by a letter. They will run out of new codes in less than 4 years.

Exam-Style Question ⊃L

At Eastinbrow School's charity fair, a stall runs a game where people choose bag. There are 10 squares in the bag, each with a different letter on it from th Contestants win £5 if they pick the letters W I N in any order and £10 if they

i) How many different sets of 3 letters can be picked?

ii) What is the probability of winning £5?

iii) What is the probability of winning £10?

iv) What is the expected win per play?

v) What would you charge per play? Give reasons for your answer. 10p.

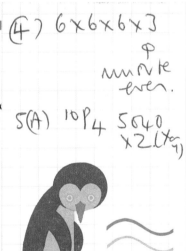

Handwritten working:

(4) $6 \times 6 \times 6 \times 3$

more even.

5(A) $^{10}P_4$ 5040 $\times 2$ (keys)

Expected win

r	0	5	10
$P(X=r)$	$\frac{713}{720}$	$\frac{1}{120}$	$\frac{1}{720}$

$E = 0 \times \frac{713}{720} + 5 \times \frac{1}{120} \times 10 \times \frac{1}{720} = \frac{1}{18} \times £1$

Expected $= 10.05p$.

$P(X=0) = 1 - \left(\frac{1}{120} + \frac{1}{720}\right)$
$= \frac{713}{720}$.

Further probability

A ABOUT THIS TOPIC

Understanding how to work out the number of choices that can be made will allow you to work out quite complicated probabilities. For some of these situations you could use a tree diagram, but using the ideas revised in the last section may be quicker so would save you time in an examination.

R REMEMBER

- Permutations and combinations, probability and tree diagrams from S1.

K KEY FACTS

- The number of ways of arranging n unlike objects in line is $n!$
- $n! = n(n-1)(n-2)\ldots \times 3 \times 2 \times 1$.
- $0! = 1$
- The number of permutations of r objects from n unlike objects is
  $^nP_r = \dfrac{n!}{(n-r)!}$ (order matters).
- The number of combinations of r objects from n unlike objects is
  $^nC_r = \dbinom{n}{r} = \dfrac{n!}{r!(n-r)!}$ (order does not matter).
- The probability that an event A occurs can often be found using
  $P(A) = \dfrac{\text{Number of ways } A \text{ can occur}}{\text{Total number of outcomes}}$.

More complicated examples of finding the number of choices

Sometimes you will need to split your working into stages.

EXAMPLE 1

There are 11 Year 7 students and nine Year 8 students in a maths club. Four of them will be chosen to be a team for a competition. The team needs to have two Year 7 students and two Year 8 students in it. How many different possible teams are there?

SOLUTION

The number of ways of choosing two Year 7 students is $^{11}C_2 = \dfrac{11!}{2!9!} = 55$.

Split the working into stages.

The order of choosing the students does not matter.

The number of ways of choosing two Year 8 students is $^9C_2 = \dfrac{9!}{2!7!} = 36$.

Each pair of Year 7 students can be teamed up with each pair of Year 8 students.

Total number of possible teams = $55 \times 36 = 1980$

EXAMPLE 2

How many numbers greater than 800 can be made from the digits 6, 7, 8, 9, 0 without repeating any digits?

SOLUTION

> Split the working into stages.

The number can have 3, 4 or 5 digits.

Any five-digit number will be greater than 800 but it cannot have 0 as the first digit so there are only four possible choices for the first digit.

Number of five-digit numbers $= 4 \times 4 \times 3 \times 2 \times 1 = 96$

> Once the 1st digit has been chosen, there are four possibilities left for the 2nd digit.

Any four-digit number will be greater than 800 but it cannot have 0 as the first digit so there are only four possible choices for the first digit.

Number of four-digit numbers $= 4 \times 4 \times 3 \times 2 = 96$

Three-digit numbers greater than 800 have to start with one of the digits 8 or 9 so there are two choices for the 1st digit. Once the first digit has been chosen, there are four possibilities left for the 3rd digit then three possibilities for the 4th digit.

Number of three-digit numbers $= 2 \times 4 \times 3 = 24$

Total number of possible numbers $= 96 + 96 + 24 = 216$

A ADVICE

It is sometimes easier, as it is in example 2, to find the number of choices by using the principle of multiplying than it is to use permutations.

! Both examples 1 and 2 involve splitting your working into stages. People sometimes get confused about whether they should multiply or add the results from the separate stages. It is the same idea as with tree diagrams:
- in example 1, each team has Year 7 **and** Year 8 students so the stages are multiplied
- in example 2, the numbers could have 3 **or** 4 **or** 5 digits so the stages are added.

Finding probabilities

You have already used

$$P(A) = \frac{\text{Number of ways } A \text{ can occur}}{\text{Total number of outcomes}}.$$

You can use combinations, factorials or permutations to find the number of ways that something can happen.

EXAMPLE 3

Six boys and nine girls work in a cafe. Three of these young people are chosen at random to wash up. What is the probability that they are all girls?

SOLUTION

> There are nine girls to choose from, the order they are chosen in does not matter.

$$P(\text{all girls}) = \frac{\text{Number of ways of getting all girls}}{\text{Total number of ways of choosing 3 young people}}$$

Number of ways of getting all girls $= {}^9C_3 = \dfrac{9!}{3!6!} = 84$

Total number of ways of choosing 3 students $= {}^{15}C_3 = \dfrac{15!}{3!12!} = 455$

> 15 young people to choose from.

$$P(\text{all girls}) = \frac{84}{455} = \frac{12}{65}$$

5 Further probability

EXAMPLE 4

A student on work experience in a nursing home takes the false teeth of four patients for cleaning. She does not make a note of which set of teeth belongs to which patient so she returns them at random. What is the probability that each patient gets their own false teeth back?

SOLUTION

$$P(\text{all get their own}) = \frac{\text{Number of ways of them all getting their own}}{\text{Total number of ways of returning the teeth}}$$

Total number of ways of returning the teeth = 4! = 24

There is only one way they can all get their own teeth, so

$$P(\text{all get their own}) = \frac{1}{24}.$$

There are four different sets of teeth the first person could get, three for the second, and so on.

A ADVICE

People sometimes get confused about whether the order matters or not. In example 3, you might have chosen all three young people at once or you might have chosen them one at a time but all that matters is which three we end up with. Example 4 is about matching teeth with people so you can imagine the people in a line being given sets of teeth, one at a time.

EXAMPLE 5

How many ways are there of choosing a chairperson and a secretary from a committee of ten people?

SOLUTION

There are ten ways of choosing the chairperson and, for each of these, there are nine ways of choosing the secretary.

Number of ways = 10 × 9 = 90

You could do $^{10}P_2$ instead. You are matching people to the two jobs.

EXAMPLE 6

In an examination students have the following inst 'Choose 4 questions from 7 in section A and choc in section B.'

A student does not follow the instructions and just ch questions from the total 11. What is the probability th questions from section A and two from section B?

(1) 4! × 6! = 24 × 720.

(3) 25 pмк; 16 free
$25C_3$ $16C_3$

∴ the same
= 2300 + 560 = 2860

41 ховб alltogether
$41C_3$

∴ $\frac{2860}{10660}$

SOLUTION

$$P(\text{choice OK}) = \frac{\text{Number of ways of 4 from A and 2 from B}}{\text{Total number of ways of choosing 6 questions}}$$

Number of ways of choosing 4 from section A $= {}^7C_4 = \dfrac{7!}{3!4!} = 35$

> Split the working into stages.

> The order of choosing the questions does not matter.

Number of ways of choosing 2 from section B $= {}^4C_2 = \dfrac{4!}{2!2!} = 6$

> Each set of section A questions can go with each pair of section B questions.

Number of ways of choosing 4 questions from section A and 2 from section B $= 35 \times 6 = 210$

Total number of ways of choosing 6 questions $= {}^{11}C_6 = \dfrac{11!}{6!5!} = 462$

$P(\text{choice OK}) = \dfrac{210}{462} = \dfrac{5}{11}$

A ADVICE

Questions that need several stages to answer, like example 6, are often split into several parts in exams. If you can't see how to do all the parts then do as many as you can, one at a time. If you have to split the question into stages for yourself then do as much as you can. You should still get marks for working even if you do not get through to the final answer.

LINKS

Statistics   Binomial distribution (S1).

Test Yourself ⊃L

1 There are 10 children in a group on a school trip: 6 boys and 4 girls. These children are told to line up with the girls at the front of the line and the boys at the end. In how many different ways can this be done?

  A 720   B 744   C 17 280   D 151 200   E 3 628 800

2 Anita is ordering lunch for a meeting. She chooses 3 kinds of sandwiches from 7 different possibilities and 2 kinds of cake from 4 different possibilities. How many different possible choices of lunch can she make?

  A 6   B 28   C 35   D 41   E 210

3 Two colours of tickets have been sold for a raffle. Pink tickets are numbered 1 to 25 and green tickets are numbered 185 to 200. Three tickets are drawn out and their owners are allowed to choose a prize. What is the probability that all 3 tickets are the same colour? (Probabilities are given to 3 s.f.)

  A 0.008 28   B 0.0113   C 0.268   D 0.286   E 0.279

4 Marius has 6 blue socks and 6 black socks in a drawer. They are all mixed up. He pulls out 4 socks at random. What is the probability that he has 2 blue socks and 2 black socks?

A $\frac{5}{11}$ B $\frac{1}{3}$ C $\frac{5}{66}$ D $\frac{2}{33}$ E $\frac{1}{33}$

5 An ordinary pack of playing cards has 52 cards in it; 13 from each suit. Four cards are dealt at random. Four of the following statements are true and one is false. Which is the false statement? (Probabilities are given to 4 s.f.)

A The probability of all 4 cards being the same colour is 0.1104.
B The probability of the cards being Jack, Queen, King, Ace (not necessarily all from the same suit) is 0.00001478.
C The probability of all 4 cards having the same value is 0.00004802.
D The probability of all 4 cards being from the same suit is 0.01056.
E The probability of the 4 cards being 2 black and 2 red is 0.3902.

Exam-Style Question 🕮

There are 20 women and 15 men working in an office. Two men and two women are going to be selected at random to attend a conference.

i)   In how many ways can this be done?

ii)   Mr Green and Mrs Green both work in the office. What is the probability that they are both selected?

The binomial distribution 6

Binomial probabilities using the formula

Where does the binomial probability formula come from?

EXAMPLE 1

A biased coin has probability 0.4 of landing heads. It is tossed three times. What is the probability that it lands heads twice?

SOLUTION

Work out these three probabilities and add them.

Each of these three probabilities is $0.6 \times 0.4^2 = 0.096$.

This can be solved by using a tree diagram.

P(2 heads) = P(HHT) or P(HTH) or P(THH)

P(HHT) = 0.4 × 0.4 × 0.6

P(HTH) = 0.4 × 0.6 × 0.4

P(THH) = 0.6 × 0.4 × 0.4

P(2 heads) = 3 × 0.096
           = 0.288

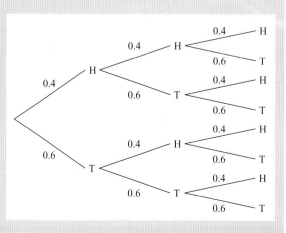

6 The binomial distribution

R RULE

$P(X = r) = {}^nC_r q^{n-r} p^r$ where $q = 1 - p$.

For the random variable X = number of heads, using the binomial probability formula with $n = 3$ and $p = 0.4$ gives this probability in one calculation.

$q = 1 - 0.4 = 0.6$

$$P(X = 2) = {}^3C_2 \times 0.6^{3-2} \times 0.4^2$$
$$= 3 \times (0.6 \times 0.4^2)$$
$$P(X = 2) = 0.288$$

This part of the formula tells you how many probabilities you would add up if you used a tree diagram.

This part of the formula tells you what each of the probabilities would be if you used a tree diagram.

A ADVICE

- When using the binomial probability formula, start by writing down what X, n, p and q stand for. Write down the formula and substitute the correct numbers into it, then use your calculator to find the answer.
- It is possible to get binomial probabilities from some graphical calculators by inputting values of n, p and r. If an examination question does not specify that the formula should be used then you can use a graphical calculator, but be aware that pressing the wrong button and so getting the wrong answer will lead to getting no marks for this part of the question. In contrast, using the formula but going wrong at the end might get you one or two method marks. If you use a calculator always write down the values of n, p and r you meant to input.

Using the binomial probability formula

The binomial probability formula speeds up some probability calculations and allows you to deal with questions where it would take too much time and space to draw a tree diagram.

EXAMPLE 2

Adam throws a die ten times and gets a score of 6 seven times. He wonders if there is something wrong with the die. What is the probability of getting seven 6s in ten throws of a fair die?

You are interested in the number of 6s.

SOLUTION

X = number of 6s scored

$n = 10, p = \frac{1}{6}$

$q = 1 - \frac{1}{6} = \frac{5}{6}$

$P(X = r) = {}^nC_r q^{n-r} p^r$

$P(X = 7) = {}^{10}C_7 \times \left(\frac{5}{6}\right)^3 \times \left(\frac{1}{6}\right)^7 = 0.000\ 248$ (3 s.f.)

The die is thrown 10 times; n is the number of trials.

If the die is fair, the probability of a 6 each time is $\frac{1}{6}$.

This is the probability of not getting a 6.

You want the probability of seven 6s so $r = 7$.

EXAMPLE 3

Adam thinks that the die should land on 6 once or twice. What is the probability of getting 6 once or twice on ten throws of a fair die?

SOLUTION

$$P(X=1) = {}^{10}C_1 \times \left(\frac{5}{6}\right)^9 \times \left(\frac{1}{6}\right)^1 = 0.323011\ldots$$

$$P(X=2) = {}^{10}C_2 \times \left(\frac{5}{6}\right)^8 \times \left(\frac{1}{6}\right)^2 = 0.290710\ldots$$

Start by working out the probability of one 6 and two 6s separately.

$$P(X=1 \text{ or } 2) = 0.323011\ldots + 0.290710\ldots = 0.613721\ldots$$

$$P(X=1 \text{ or } 2) = 0.614 \text{ (3 s.f.)}$$

Do not round before the final answer.

Finding the probability of 'at least one'

A ADVICE

If you are asked to find the probability of at least one 'success', it is usually quickest to find the probability of no successes and subtract this from 1. There are either no successes or there is at least one, so these probabilities add to 1.

EXAMPLE 4

A multiple choice test has five questions, each with four possible answers. A student guesses all the answers. What is the probability he gets at least one correct?

SOLUTION

X = number of correct answers

$$n=5, \quad p=\tfrac{1}{4}, \quad q=\tfrac{3}{4}$$

5 questions, $\frac{1}{4}$ chance of guessing each one correctly.

$$P(X=r) = {}^nC_r q^{n-r} p^r$$

Find the probability of getting none right first.

$$P(X=0) = {}^5C_0 \left(\frac{3}{4}\right)^5 \left(\frac{1}{4}\right)^0 = 0.237304\ldots$$

$$P(\text{at least one right}) = 1 - 0.237304\ldots = 0.762695\ldots \approx 0.763$$

Recognising situations which are binomial

In an exam paper of mixed questions, it is not always obvious when you should use the binomial probability formula. It is even less obvious when using probability in real life. The key facts at the start of this section will help you to decide if it is a binomial situation.

EXAMPLE 5

Frooties are a type of fruit-flavoured sweet; they are sold in tubes of 14 sweets. Anya likes the red ones. Overall, 20% of Frooties produced are red. What is the distribution of the number of red sweets in a tube? What assumptions have you made in answering this question?

SOLUTION

X = number of red sweets in a tube

$n = 14$

$p = 0.2$

$X \sim B(14, 0.2)$

> *n* is the number of trials. There are 14 sweets in a tube and checking each one is a 'trial'.

> The proportion of red sweets is 0.2.

> This is how you write that X has a binomial distribution with $n = 14$ and $p = 0.2$.

Assumptions: The probability of each sweet being red is 0.2. This probability is independent of whether other sweets in the tube are red or not.

> This may not be the case. It depends on how well the sweets are mixed before they are packed.

 Watch out very carefully to see if the probability of 'success' is the same each time, and independent of what has happened in previous trials.

EXAMPLE 6

Half the students in a class of 30 are girls. The teacher chooses students at random to answer questions but does not ask the same student twice in a lesson. He asks 12 questions in a lesson. Explain why you could not use a binomial distribution to find the probability that six girls and six boys are questioned.

SOLUTION

The probability of the first student being a girl is $\frac{15}{30} = 0.5$ but, once the first student has been asked, the probability of the second student being a girl will be different because there are only 29 students to choose from. For a binomial distribution, the probability must be the same each time.

 LINKS

Statistics   Poisson distribution (S2), Normal distribution (S2).

Test Yourself ▷L

1 A radio station is having a phone-in programme. They guarantee that exactly 70% of calls, chosen at random, will be answered. 5 friends ring up. What is the probability that exactly 2 of them have their calls answered?

   A 0   B 0.01323   C 0.1323   D 0.3087   E 0.49

2 'One-fifth of all chocolate bars contain a winning ticket' says the advert. Mark is determined to get a winning ticket. He buys 10 chocolate bars. What is the probability that he has one or two winning tickets? (You should assume that the advert is true and that each bar of chocolate is equally likely to contain a winning ticket. Some answers are rounded to 4 d.p.)

   A 0.0336   B 0.0811   C 0.24   D 0.5704   E 1

3 There are two tills in a shop. One of the assistants thinks that each customer is equally likely to go to either till. If she is right, what is the probability that, for the next 10 customers, 5 go to each till?

A $\frac{1}{1024}$ B $\frac{63}{256}$ C $\frac{1}{32}$ D $\frac{1}{16}$ E 1

4 95% of the ballpoint pens produced in a factory work. They sell them in packs of 6 pens and give a money-back guarantee if a customer buys a pack that contains any pens that do not work. What percentage of packs will they have to refund money on? (You should assume that the faulty pens are thoroughly mixed with the working pens before packing.)

1 – all work.

A 30%   B 26.5%   C 26.4%   D 23.2%   E 5%

5 The binomial distribution cannot be used for four of the random variables described below. It can be used for one of them. Which one can the binomial distribution be used for?

A A fair die is thrown 15 times. The random variable is the score on the die.   *1/6*

B A bag contains a fixed number of balls. Some are black and the rest are white. A ball is taken without looking and its colour noted. It is replaced and the balls are mixed. This process takes place 5 times. The random variable is the number of times a white ball is seen.

C A fair coin is tossed until it lands heads. The random variable is the number of tosses.

D Students take a 40-question multiple choice test, for which they have revised. Each question has 5 possible answers. The random variable is the number of questions a student gets right.

E Rose opens a box of chocolates and eats them at random. There are 14 chocolates in the box, 4 are plain and the rest are milk. Rose eats 8 chocolates. The random variable is the number of plain chocolates she eats.

Exam-Style Question

In the 17th century, people used to gamble on whether there would be at least one double 6 in 24 throws of a pair of dice.

i) Show that the probability of a double 6 when you throw a pair of fair dice is $\frac{1}{36}$.

ii) Find the probability of exactly one double 6 in 24 throws of the pair of dice.

iii) Find the probability of at least one double 6 in 24 throws of the pair of dice.

Binomial distribution: expectation and use of tables

A ABOUT THIS TOPIC

Using the binomial probability formula enables you to work out the probability of one outcome. If you want several outcomes combined together, it is much quicker to use cumulative binomial tables. You can find these in the *Companion to Advanced Mathematics and Statistics*, and they will be available to you in the examination. Using statistical tables is essential for your exam in addition to being a useful skill if you go on to use statistics beyond Advanced level.

R REMEMBER

- Combinations, probability, tree diagrams, discrete random variables and the binomial distribution from S1.
- The expectation of a random variable, X, is denoted $E(X)$; the symbol μ is often used to stand for the expectation. It is sometimes called 'the expected value' or 'the mean'.
- The conditions for a binomial distribution (page 77, **Key facts**).
- You write $X \sim B(n, p)$ to show that X has a binomial distribution.
- $P(X = r) = {}^nC_r\, q^{n-r}p^r$ where $q = 1 - p$, $r = 0, 1, 2, ..., n$.

K KEY FACTS

- The expectation of a binomial random variable is $E(X) = np$.
- Cumulative binomial probability tables give values of $P(X \leq x)$. This is the total probability $P(X = 0) + P(X = 1) + ... + P(X = x)$.

The expectation of a binomial random variable

You know that to find the expectation of a discrete random variable you need to multiply each possible value by its probability and add them up. For a binomial discrete random variable, this simplifies to:

For $X \sim B(n, p)$, $E(X) = np$.

EXAMPLE 1

A bank claims that 95% of callers to its helpline wait less than four minutes to speak to an adviser. A random sample of 40 callers is surveyed to find out how long it took before they were able to speak to an adviser. What is the expected number in the sample that waited at least four minutes?

SOLUTION

For a random sample, it is reasonable to assume that the probability for each caller of waiting longer than four minutes is the same and independent of other callers.

X = number of callers in a sample who waited at least 4 minutes

p = probability of a caller waiting at least 4 minutes = 0.05

$X \sim B(40, 0.05)$

$E(X) = np = 40 \times 0.05 = 2$

> Remember to say what any letters you introduce stand for.

> Show that you know this is a binomial distribution.

> '95% less than 4 minutes' means '5% at least 4 minutes'.

> Use the formula for expectation of a binomial distribution.

- If all callers one evening were surveyed instead of a random sample, it would not be reasonable to assume that the probability of each one waiting at least four minutes was the same. If one caller takes a long time on the phone, this will make the waiting time of the ones who come after him (or her) longer.
- The expected value might not have a very high probability of occurring and it need not be a whole number.

EXAMPLE 2

For the sample in example 1, what is the probability that exactly two callers in this sample waited at least four minutes?

SOLUTION

$X \sim B(40, 0.05)$

$P(X = r) = {}^{n}C_{r} q^{n-r} p^{r}$ where $q = 0.95$

$P(X = 2) = {}^{40}C_{2} \times 0.95^{38} \times 0.05^{2} = 0.277\,671... \approx 0.2777$

> Example 1 shows what the letters stand for, so this is not repeated here.

> Putting the numbers into the binomial probability formula then using a calculator to get the answer.

Using binomial tables

The binomial probability formula is quick to use if you just want a single probability. To save work when dealing with situations where several probabilities would need to be added, binomial probability tables can be used. This is shown in the next two examples.

 A **ADVICE**

The binomial tables you get in the exam are cumulative probability tables. This is a similar idea to cumulative frequency; they tell you the individual probabilities added up so you can find $P(X \leqslant x)$.

6 The binomial distribution

EXAMPLE 3

An office has eight identical printers. On any given day, the probability of any one of them being faulty is 0.15, independently of the others. What is the probability that, on a given day, three or fewer of the printers are faulty?

SOLUTION

X = the number of faulty printers on a given day.

Write the information in symbols.

$n = 8$, $p = 0.15$, $q = 0.85$, where p is the probability of a printer being faulty.

X has a binomial distribution as the probability of each printer being faulty is the same so $X \sim B(8, 0.15)$.

You want $P(X \leqslant 3)$.

Write what you are asked to find in symbols.

The extreme left-hand column gives the value of n.

The top row in the tables gives values of p.

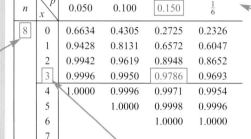

n	x	0.050	0.100	0.150	$\frac{1}{6}$
8	0	0.6634	0.4305	0.2725	0.2326
	1	0.9428	0.8131	0.6572	0.6047
	2	0.9942	0.9619	0.8948	0.8652
	3	0.9996	0.9950	0.9786	0.9693
	4	1.0000	0.9996	0.9971	0.9954
	5		1.0000	0.9998	0.9996
	6			1.0000	1.0000
	7				

The second column gives values of x so that you can read across to find $P(X \leqslant x)$.

$P(X \leqslant 3) = 0.9786$

A ADVICE

The tables only give $P(X \leqslant x)$. If the probability you want is not written in this form, write down the possible values to help you see how to use the tables to find it.

Be careful when writing the probability you want as an inequality. Some commonly used phrases, and how they translate to symbols, are listed in this table.

Phrase	Less than 3	No more than 3	Up to 3	More than 3	No less than 3	At least 3
Symbols	$X < 3$	$X \leqslant 3$	$X \leqslant 3$	$X > 3$	$X \geqslant 3$	$X \geqslant 3$
Values (X is an integer)	0, 1, 2	0, 1, 2, 3	0, 1, 2, 3	4, 5, ...	3, 4, ...	3, 4, ...

EXAMPLE 4

18 people are playing the chocolate game. Players need to throw a 6 on a fair die to get a chance to eat some chocolate. In the first round each player throws the die once. What is the probability that more than six players throw a 6?

SOLUTION

X = the number of players who throw a 6; this has a binomial distribution as each one has the same chance of throwing a 6.

$n = 18$, $p = \frac{1}{6}$, $q = \frac{5}{6}$, where p = probability of throwing a 6.

$X \sim B\left(18, \frac{1}{6}\right)$

You want $P(X > 6)$. Possible values are 7, 8, 9, 10, ..., 18. Hence, not 0, 1, 2, ..., 6.

$P(X > 6) = 1 - P(X \leq 6) = 1 - 0.9794 = 0.0206$

> Write down the possible values to help you see how to use the tables.

n	x \ p	0.050	0.100	0.150	$\frac{1}{6}$	0.200
18	0	0.3972	0.1501	0.0536	0.0376	0.0180
	1	0.7735	0.4503	0.2241	0.1728	0.0991
	2	0.9419	0.7338	0.4794	0.4027	0.2713
	3	0.9891	0.9018	0.7202	0.6479	0.5010
	4	0.9985	0.9718	0.8794	0.8318	0.7164
	5	0.9998	0.9936	0.9581	0.9347	0.8671
	6	1.0000	0.9988	0.9882	0.9794	0.9487
	7		0.9998	0.9973	0.9947	0.9837
	8		1.0000	0.9995	0.9989	0.9957

It is also possible to use cumulative binomial probability tables to find the probability of a random variable being between two values.

EXAMPLE 5

For the random variable, X, in example 4, find $P(3 \leq X < 7)$.

SOLUTION

$P(3 \leq X < 7) = P(X \leq 6) - P(X < 3)$

> $(X < 3)$ is the same as $(X \leq 2)$.

> The possible values are 3, 4, 5, 6.

$P(3 \leq X < 7) = P(X \leq 6) - P(X \leq 2) = 0.9794 - 0.4027 = 0.5767$

> ⚠ Remember tables can only give you $P(X \leq x)$ so you need to have probabilities with 'less than or equal to'.

LINKS

Statistics   Binomial hypothesis testing (S1), Poisson distribution (S2), Normal distribution (S2).

Test Yourself

1 In the game 'Find the lady', the player has to say which one of 3 shuffled cards is the queen. The cards are face down. A player plays this game 8 times. What is the expected number of times he wins, assuming that he is guessing?

A 2   B 2.5   C $2\frac{2}{3}$ D 3   E 4

2 X is a binomial random variable. Below are five pairs of inequalities; one in words and one in symbols. Four of the pairs are equivalent and one pair is not equivalent. Which is the pair that is not equivalent?

A X is no more than 6; $X \leqslant 6$.   B X is at least 5; $X \geqslant 5$.
C X is more than 6; $X > 6$.   D X is not less than 7; $X \geqslant 7$.
E X is at most 7; $X > 7$.

3 X is a binomial random variable. Below are five statements about probabilities involving inequalities. Four of them are true and one is false. Which is the false one?

A $P(X \geqslant 4) = 1 - P(X \leqslant 4)$ B $P(X < 3) = P(X \leqslant 2)$
C $P(X > 5) = 1 - P(X \leqslant 5)$ D $P(3 < X < 8) = P(X \leqslant 7) - P(X \leqslant 3)$
E $P(2 \leqslant X \leqslant 6) = P(X \leqslant 6) - P(X \leqslant 1)$

4 In the UK, 20% of children aged 2–15 years have asthma. Two adults are planning to take 12 children from this age group on a trip. Assuming that the children are a random sample from the population, what is the probability that no more than 2 out of the 12 children will suffer from asthma?

A 0.2749   B 0.2835   C 0.4417   D 0.5583   E 0.5584

5 There are 10 hurdles in a race. A particular runner has a 65% chance of clearing any one of them. This probability is not affected by whether or not she has cleared the previous hurdles. What is the probability that she clears more than half the hurdles, but not all of them? (All answers are rounded to 3 d.p.)

A 0.500   B 0.627   C 0.738   D 0.741   E 0.892

Exam-Style Question

A computer chooses 12 digits at random. Each digit can be either 0 or 1 and is equally likely to be either of these. The computer then adds all 12 digits to give a total.

i)   Explain why the total of these digits, X, is binomially distributed, $X \sim B(n, p)$, with $n = 12$ and $p = \frac{1}{2}$.

ii)   What is the expected value of the total?

iii) Find the probability that the total is at least 9.

Hypothesis testing using the binomial distribution

1-tail tests using probability

A ABOUT THIS TOPIC

Statistical hypothesis testing is used in scientific and medical research, in industry and in the social sciences. A hypothesis test assesses observed data to answer the question: 'How likely is it that this happened by chance?' To take a simple example, if a coin lands heads 14 times and tails 6 times, is there enough evidence to convince us that it is biased?

R REMEMBER

- Binomial probability, including use of tables, from S1.
- Conditional probability from S1.

K KEY FACTS

- In hypothesis testing for a binomial distribution, you use evidence from a sample to make a decision about the probability of 'success' for the whole population.
- For a hypothesis test using the binomial distribution, the null hypothesis is written in the form $H_0 : p = 0.3$ (or some other specific value).
- There should be a statement defining what p stands for.
  For example, $p =$ the probability of a light bulb lasting less than 100 hours.
- For a 1-tail test **either** the alternative hypothesis that goes with the example null hypothesis above is $H_1 : p > 0.3$ **or** it is $H_1 : p < 0.3$.
- Assuming the null hypothesis is true, the probability of the observed value (and those more extreme) is calculated. This probability is compared with the significance level of the test which is often set at 5% or 1%.
- If the probability is smaller than the significance level, the null hypothesis is rejected. Otherwise the null hypothesis is accepted.

A ADVICE

You need to set out your working carefully when testing a hypothesis. This will help you to organise your thinking as well as getting you marks in the examination. The process will be shown, step by step, using the following example.

EXAMPLE 1

The head of a large school announces that to give equal opportunities to all students, the School Council will be chosen at random from all the students, instead of students being elected to the Council, because an election is biased towards popular students. There are equal numbers of boys and girls in the school but the School Council chosen consists of ten girls and four boys. Is there evidence (at the 5% level) of a bias towards girls in the selection process?

Deciding what the hypotheses are

If there is no bias, each vacancy is equally likely to be filled by a boy as it is to be filled by a girl. Let p = the probability of a vacancy being filled by a girl. The two possibilities are:

$$p = \tfrac{1}{2} \text{ and } p > \tfrac{1}{2}$$

> You are looking for evidence of a bias towards girls.

The first of these gives the benefit of the doubt to the head so it is the null hypothesis. The hypotheses are:

$$\left. \begin{aligned} H_0 &: p = \tfrac{1}{2} \\ H_1 &: p > \tfrac{1}{2} \end{aligned} \right\} \begin{aligned} &\text{where } p \text{ is the probability of a girl} \\ &\text{being chosen to fill a vacancy} \end{aligned}$$

A ADVICE

- For a hypothesis test using the binomial distribution, the null hypothesis must be p = a specific value.
- You must say what p stands for.
- You will get marks in the exam for writing down the hypotheses correctly even if you go wrong with the rest of the question.

Calculating an appropriate probability

> The null hypothesis, H_0, says that there is no bias.

There are 14 vacancies. Assuming the null hypothesis is true, the number of girls on the council, X, would have a binomial distribution.

$$X \sim B(14, 0.5) \text{ if } H_0 \text{ is true.}$$

$X = 10$ and this raised a doubt as to whether H_0 is true; you would be even more doubtful if there were more girls, so find $P(X \geqslant 10)$.

> Possible values are 10, 11, 12, 13, 14; that is, not 0 to 9 inclusive.

$$P(X \geqslant 10) = 1 - P(X \leqslant 9)$$

> Remember probabilities in tables must use $\leqslant$.

From binomial tables for $n = 14$ and $p = 0.5$,

$$P(X \leqslant 9) = 0.9102 \text{ so } P(X \geqslant 10) = 1 - 0.9102 = 0.0898.$$

 Do not work out the probability of just one value, $P(X = 10)$ in example 1, because the probability for any particular value of X can be very small (especially if n is large). You could then be in the position of deciding that none of the outcomes are likely, but something has to happen. Always work out the probability of the **observed outcome together with** those which cast even more doubt on the null hypothesis.

Making a decision and what it means

$P(X \geqslant 10) = 0.0898$. This is not a large probability but nor is it all that small; it is about 1 in 11. This means that, if the selection process were unbiased, we would get ten, or more, girls once every 11 times. Is that unlikely enough for you to decide that the selection process is biased?

The level at which you decide 'This is so unlikely that I do not believe the null hypothesis is true after all' is called the significance level of the test. In this case it was set at 5%, or 1 in 20. Since getting 10 or more girls was more likely than this, you accept the null hypothesis, that $p = \frac{1}{2}$, and reject the alternative hypothesis, that $p > \frac{1}{2}$. There is not sufficient evidence of a bias towards girls at the 5% level of significance.

You are usually given the significance level in the question but sometimes you may be asked what it means as well.

A ADVICE

- Working out a probability when hypothesis testing helps to decide whether what actually happened could have just happened by chance if the null hypothesis is true.
- Compare the probability you work out with the significance level and reject H_0 if the probability is smaller than the significance level.
- Relate your decision to the original situation; don't just say 'accept H_0'.

Putting it all together

All the stages in a hypothesis test are shown together in the following example.

EXAMPLE 2

A plastic moulding machine has been producing 30% misshapes. After the machine is serviced, a sample of 20 objects is taken and two of them are misshapes. Is there evidence, at the 5% level of significance, that the machine is producing fewer misshapes?

SOLUTION

$$\left. \begin{array}{l} H_0 : p = 0.3 \\ H_1 : p < 0.3 \end{array} \right\} \text{ where } p \text{ is the proportion of} \atop \text{misshapes produced by the machine}$$

Remember the null hypothesis starts $p = ...$

You were asked to look for evidence that the machine is producing fewer misshapes.

Remember to say what letters stand for.

X = number of misshapes in a sample of 20

If the null hypothesis is true, X has a binomial distribution with $n = 20, p = 0.3$.
$X \sim B(20, 0.3)$

Write down the distribution X would have if H_0 were true.

$X = 2$ is what happened. A smaller value of X would make you believe the alternative hypothesis even more.

You need to find $P(X \leqslant 2)$

From tables, $P(X \leqslant 2) = 0.0355 = 3.55\%$.
This is smaller than 5% so reject H_0.

There is sufficient evidence, at the 5% level of significance, that the machine is producing fewer misshapes.

State the conclusion in the context of the original question.

> ⚠ • You know that 2 out of 20 in the sample were misshapes. That is 10% of the sample, but you want to know about the percentage of misshapes in **all** the objects the machine produces. Is it likely to be less than 30%, or have you just got a good sample by chance?
> • Statistical hypothesis testing does not allow you to be sure whether the machine is producing fewer misshapes or not; it provides evidence to help you make a decision.

A diagrammatic representation

For the situation in example 2, the probabilities for the different values that X can take, if the null hypothesis is true, are shown in the vertical line chart.

$P(X \leqslant 2)$ is shaded in blue. The total of these probabilities is less than 5%.

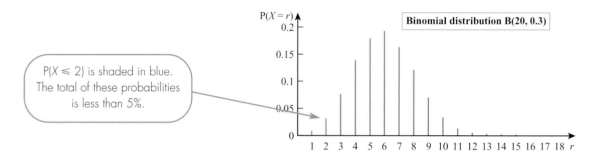

A ADVICE

You will use tables to test hypotheses in exams but you may find a mental picture of the individual probabilities, as above, helps you to see what is happening.

LINKS

Statistics   Hypothesis testing (S2, S3 and S4).

Test Yourself ▶L

The following situation is for **questions 1–4**. A local authority claims that two-thirds of households in their area recycle glass. An environmentalist thinks that this is based on out of date data and that more households now recycle glass. He takes a random sample of 20 households and finds that 16 recycle glass. He wishes to test, at the 5% level of significance, whether there is evidence that more than two-thirds of households in the area recycle glass.

1   Which of these gives the hypotheses for the test which the environmentalist uses?
In each case, p = proportion of households in the area that recycle glass.

   A $\quad H_0 : p > \frac{2}{3}$ B $\quad H_0 : p = \frac{2}{3}$ C $\quad H_0 : p = \frac{2}{3}$ D $\quad H_0 : p < \frac{2}{3}$ E $\quad H_0 : p = 0.8$
       $\quad H_1 : p = \frac{2}{3}$ $\quad H_1 : p > \frac{2}{3}$ $\quad H_1 : p \neq \frac{2}{3}$ $\quad H_1 : p > \frac{2}{3}$ $\quad H_1 : p < 0.8$

2   X = the number of households in a sample that recycle glass. Which one of the following probabilities does the environmentalist require, in order to decide between the null and alternative hypotheses?
   A $P(X > 16)$ B $P(X = 16)$ C $P(X \geqslant 16)$ D $P(X < 16)$ E $P(X \leqslant 16)$

*Before doing **question 3**, you need to get **question 2** correct then find that probability.*

3 Which is the decision the environmentalist should come to, with the correct reason?

  A Accept H_0 because the probability from question 2 is more than 5%.

  B Reject H_0 because the probability from question 2 is more than 5%.

  C Accept H_0 because the probability from question 2 is different from 5%.

  D Reject H_0 because the probability from question 2 is different from 5%.

  E Reject H_0 because $\frac{16}{20} > \frac{2}{3}$.

4 Which of the following is the best statement of the final conclusion to the test?

  A Accept H_0 at the 5% significance level.

  B Reject H_0.

  C It is certain that no more than two-thirds of households recycle glass.

  D There is insufficient evidence, at the 5% significance level, to justify the claim that more than two-thirds of households recycle glass.

  E Accept the alternative hypothesis at the 5% significance level.

5 A newspaper claims that a third of sandwiches from a local shop are contaminated with bacteria. An independent researcher tests a random sample of 20 sandwiches from the shop and finds that one of them is contaminated. This provides evidence, at the 5% level of significance, that less than a third of the shop's sandwiches are contaminated. Which one of the following inequalities leads you to this conclusion?

  A $\frac{1}{20} \leqslant 5\%$ B $\frac{1}{20} < \frac{1}{3}$ C $0.0176 < 0.05$ D $0.0030 < 0.05$

  E $0.0033 < 0.05$

Exam-Style Question ▷L

A medical researcher claims that a new treatment is effective in 75% of cases. In an independent trial, a sample of 20 people try the treatment and it is effective for 12 of them. A suitable statistical test will be carried out to see whether there is evidence that the researcher's claims are exaggerated.

i)   Write down suitable null and alternative hypotheses.

ii) Carry out the test at the 5% level of significance, stating your conclusions clearly. You should assume that each person's response to the treatment is independent of the others.

iii) Why is the assumption of independence important? Is it likely to be true?

Critical values and critical regions

Critical values are important because they allow you to establish when you would reject the null hypothesis before you actually collect the data. This has the advantage of enabling non-statisticians to collect the data and see what it means. Deciding criteria for rejecting H_0 in advance has another advantage: it reduces the temptation to adjust the significance level to give the result you want.

- Assuming the null hypothesis is true, large (**or** small) values of the number of successes, X, are found, such that these have a total probability of the significance level of the test (or slightly less). This is the *critical region*.
- If the observed value of the number of successes, X, is in the critical region, the null hypothesis is rejected. Otherwise it is accepted.

- Binomial probability, including use of tables, conditional probability, and 1-tail tests from S1.
- In hypothesis testing for a binomial distribution, you use evidence from a sample to make a decision about the probability of 'success' for the whole population.
- For a hypothesis test using the binomial distribution, the null hypothesis is written in the form $H_0: p = 0.3$ (or some other specific value).
- There should be a statement defining what p stands for.
  For example, p = the probability of a light bulb lasting less than 100 hours.
- For a 1-tail test, **either** the alternative hypothesis that goes with the example null hypothesis above is $H_1: p > 0.3$ **or** it is $H_1: p < 0.3$.

Critical region for an alternative hypothesis involving 'less than'

EXAMPLE 1

An IT company knows its customers are dissatisfied with the helpline so it decides to train its staff. First the company surveys its customers and finds that 30% of them are dissatisfied with the helpline. Following training for the staff on the helpline, the company surveys a random sample of 19 customers and finds that three of them are dissatisfied with the helpline. It carries out a suitable hypothesis test.

i) State the null and alternative hypotheses.

ii) Find the critical region for the relevant test at the 5% level of significance.

iii) Use the critical region to decide whether there is evidence that fewer of the customers are dissatisfied with the helpline.

SOLUTION

i) p = the proportion of customers who are dissatisfied with the helpline.

The hypotheses are:

$H_0 : p = 0.3$
$H_1 : p < 0.3$

> The company is looking for evidence that fewer customers are dissatisfied.

> Say what X and p stand for.

X = the number of dissatisfied customers in a sample of 19 customers.

ii) If the null hypothesis is true, X will have a binomial distribution with $n = 19$ and $p = 0.3$. This is written $X \sim B(19, 0.3)$.

To find the critical region, it is helpful to have a mental picture of the probability distribution.

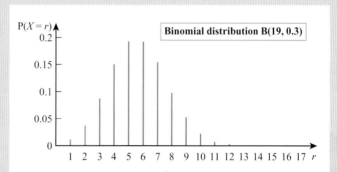

The null hypothesis will be rejected if there is a small number of dissatisfied customers in the sample. Your task is to find low possible values of X with a **total probability** of 5%. This is sometimes called the lower tail.

The binomial probability tables give total probabilities; the table for $n = 19$ and $p = 0.3$ is shown here.

n	x	0.050	0.100	0.150	$\frac{1}{6}$	0.200	0.250	0.300
19	0	0.3774	0.1351	0.0456	0.0313	0.0144	0.0042	0.0011
	1	0.7547	0.4203	0.1985	0.1502	0.0829	0.0310	0.0104
	2	0.9335	0.7054	0.4413	0.3643	0.2369	0.1113	0.0462
	3	0.9868	0.8850	0.6841	0.6070	0.4551	0.2631	0.1332
	4	0.9980	0.9648	0.8556	0.8011	0.6733	0.4654	0.2822
	5	0.9998	0.9914	0.9463	0.9176	0.8369	0.6678	0.4739

$P(X \leqslant 2) = 0.0462$
$P(X \leqslant 3) = 0.1332$

> You need to write down both these probabilities, one each side of 5%, so that it is clear how you chose your critical region.

The first of these probabilities is 4.62% and the second is 13.32%.

It is not possible to get exactly 5% so go for 4.62%.

The critical region is $X \leqslant 2$.

iii) The number of dissatisfied customers in the sample of 19 was 3 so $X = 3$. This is not in the critical region so you accept the null hypothesis. There is not enough evidence, at the 5% level, to show that there has been a reduction in the number of dissatisfied customers.

It is almost never possible to get exactly 5% (or whatever the significance level is) when finding a critical region for a binomial hypothesis test. You should always go for a probability lower than the significance level, not the one nearest to it. In example 1, the 10% significance level critical region would still be $X \leqslant 2$ because $X \leqslant 3$ has a probability of 13.32% and this is too high.

Critical region for an alternative hypothesis involving 'more than'

EXAMPLE 2

A die is being used to play a game. It is thrown 16 times and seems to be landing on 6 more often than on any of the other numbers.
i) Find the critical region for a 2.5% significance level test to see whether there is evidence that the die is biased towards 6.
ii) The die lands on 6 eight times. Use your critical region to conduct the test.

SOLUTION

i) The hypotheses are: $\left. \begin{array}{l} H_0 : p = \frac{1}{6} \\ H_1 : p > \frac{1}{6} \end{array} \right\}$ p = probability the die lands on 6.

> Assume the die is fair but look for evidence that it is biased towards landing on 6.

X = the number of 6s in 16 throws.

If the null hypothesis, H_0, is true, X has a binomial distribution with $n = 16$ and $p = \frac{1}{6}$.

That is, $X \sim B\left(16, \frac{1}{6}\right)$.

A large number of throws landing 6 will provide evidence that $p > \frac{1}{6}$ and so lead to your rejecting the null hypothesis, H_0.

You need to find a value of x with $P(X \geqslant x) = 0.025 = 2.5\%$.

> You need to write down both these probabilities, one each side of 0.975, so that it is clear how you chose your critical region.

The probabilities in the table are $P(X \leqslant x)$ so look for $1 - 0.025 = 0.975$ or more.

$P(X \leqslant 5) = 0.9622$
$P(X \leqslant 6) = 0.9899$

Work with the one bigger than 0.975 to get your critical region.

> X could be 7, 8, 9, ...,16.

$P(X \text{ is not} \leqslant 6) = 1 - 0.9899$
i.e. $P(X \geqslant 7) = 0.0101 = 1.01\%$.

n	x	$\frac{1}{6}$
16	0	0.0541
	1	0.2272
	2	0.4868
	3	0.7291
	4	0.8866
	5	0.9622
	6	0.9899
	7	0.9979

You need a probability of 2.5%, or less, and so the critical region is $X \geqslant 7$. This is sometimes called the *upper tail*.

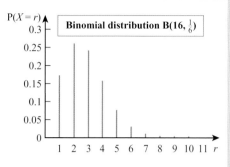

ii) The critical region is $X \geqslant 7$. $X = 8$ is in this critical region so leads to rejection of H_0. There is sufficient evidence, at the 2.5% level, that the die is biased in favour of rolling a 6.

A ADVICE

Once you know the critical region, you do not need to do any further calculations to carry out the hypothesis test. If you had not worked out the critical region in part **i)** you could have done the test by working out $P(X \geqslant 8)$ in part **ii)**.

Empty critical region

EXAMPLE 3

10% of the population of a country suffer from a particular chronic disease. Following a local public health campaign to reduce levels of the disease, a health worker wants to know whether the campaign has been effective. She decides to take a random sample of 20 people and test them for the disease to see if there is evidence, at the 5% level, that the proportion of people with the disease has dropped. Find the critical region.

SOLUTION

The hypotheses are:
$$H_0 : p = 0.1$$
$$H_1 : p < 0.1$$

> She is looking for evidence that the proportion has dropped below 10%.

where p is the proportion of people in the area with the disease, and X = the number of people with the disease in a sample of 20.

If the null hypothesis, H_0, is true, X has a binomial distribution with $n = 20$ and $p = 0.1$, which can be written $X \sim B(20, 0.1)$.

$P(X \leqslant 0) = 0.1216 = 12.16\%$

This is more than 5% so the critical region is empty.

A ADVICE

The empty critical region means you cannot get enough evidence to reject H_0, at the 5% level, from a sample of 20 people. You need a larger sample for this test.

n	x	p 0.050	0.100
20	0	0.3585	0.1216
	1	0.7358	0.3917

LINKS

Statistics   Hypothesis testing (S2, S3 and S4).

Test Yourself ⊃L

1 A binomial hypothesis test is conducted with a sample size n, significance level 5% and hypotheses: $H_0 : p = \frac{1}{3}$, $H_1 : p > \frac{1}{3}$. X is the number of successes. Four of the following statements about critical regions are true and one is false. Which statement is false?

  A There is only one value in the critical region for $n = 12$.

  B If $n = 18$, the critical region is the same as it would be for a significance level of 10%.

  C $n = 8$ is the smallest value of n for which the critical region is non-empty.

  D For $n = 16$, the critical region is $X \leq 2$.

  E The critical region is the same for each of $n = 8, 9, 10, 11, 12$.

2 A national survey of university students shows that 55% of them do paid work to help finance their studies. A university tutor suspects that a lower percentage of students in her university do paid work. A random sample of 18 students from the university is taken. X is the number of students in a sample who do paid work. Which of the following is the critical region for a test, at the 10% level, to see whether there is evidence to support the tutor's suspicions?

  A $X \leq 1$ B $X \leq 3$ C $X \leq 6$ D $X \leq 7$ E $X \leq 9$

3 A binomial hypothesis test is conducted with a sample size n, significance level 5% and hypotheses: $H_0 : p = \frac{1}{3}$, $H_1 : p > \frac{1}{3}$. X is the number of successes. Four of the following statements about critical regions are true and one is false. Which statement is false?

  A To help you find the critical region, you should look for a probability of 0.95, or more, in the cumulative binomial probability tables.

  B The critical region for $n = 18$ is $X \geq 9$.

  C The smallest value of n with a non-empty critical region is $n = 3$.

  D The critical region for $n = 8$ is $X \geq 6$.

  E The critical region is the same for each of $n = 14, 15, 16$.

4 75% of all adults in the United Kingdom owned or used a mobile phone in May 2003 (Oftel survey). Kelvin suspected that now, in his area, a higher proportion of adults use a mobile phone. He asked a random sample of 17 adults whether they owned a mobile phone, or used one in the last month. X is the number of adults in a sample who owned or used a mobile phone. What is the critical region for a hypothesis test at the 5% level of significance?

  A $X \leq 9$ B $X \geq 13$ C $X \leq 16$ D $X \geq 16$ E $X = 17$

Exam-Style Question ⊃L

An election leaflet produced by the Purple Party for a local election claims that, in a recent survey, only 30% of voters said they intended to vote for the rival Beige Party. The Beige Party thinks they have more support than this; in a random sample of 18 voters from the local area, 9 of them say they will vote for the Beige Party.

i)   Carry out a suitable hypothesis test at the 5% level of significance, stating your hypotheses and conclusions clearly.

Following a scandal reported in the press, the Beige Party are concerned that their level of support may have dropped below 30%. They intend to survey a random sample of n voters to test whether there is evidence for this, at the 1% level of significance.

ii) Show that, if $n = 10$, the critical region for this test is empty.

iii) What is the critical region when $n = 20$?

iv) What is the smallest value of n that gives a non-empty critical region?

2-tail tests

A ABOUT THIS TOPIC

The previous two sections about hypothesis testing have involved only 1-tail tests. In a 1-tail test, the alternative hypothesis is either that $p > a$ particular value **or** that $p < a$ particular value. For a 2-tail test, the alternative hypothesis is $p \neq a$ particular value; so you are looking for evidence of any difference rather than for evidence of a difference in a particular direction.

R REMEMBER

- Binomial probability, including use of tables, conditional probability, 1-tail tests, and critical regions from S1.
- In hypothesis testing for a binomial distribution, you use evidence from a sample to make a decision about the probability of success for the whole population.
- For a hypothesis test using the binomial distribution, the null hypothesis is written in the form $H_0: p = 0.3$ (or some other specific value).
- There should be a statement defining what p stands for.
  For example, p = the probability of a light bulb lasting less than 100 hours.

K KEY FACTS

- For a 2-tail test the alternative hypothesis that goes with the null hypothesis $H_0: p = 0.3$ is $H_1: p \neq 0.3$ (this includes both possibilities: $p > 0.3$ and $p < 0.3$).
- 2-tail tests can be carried out using either probability or critical regions.
- The significance level for a 2-tail test is split into two halves: one half for each tail.

Symmetrical and asymmetrical binomial distributions

The binomial distribution is symmetrical if $p = 0.5$. It is skewed for other values of p. This is illustrated in the vertical line graphs overleaf.

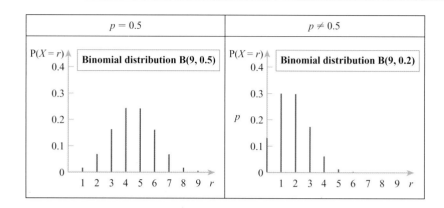

Critical region for a symmetrical 2-tail test

EXAMPLE 1

As part of an engineering project, Alicia invents a machine that is intended to replace tossing a coin at the start of a sports match. The machine should show 'heads' or 'tails' with equal probability. To test it for bias, she will run it 20 times. For what numbers of 'heads' will she conclude that it is biased, at the 5% level of significance?

SOLUTION

$H_0 : p = 0.5$
$H_1 : p \neq 0.5$ } where p is the probability of 'heads' on each run.

If the machine is unbiased, the probability of 'heads' on each go is 0.5.

She is looking for evidence of bias in either direction.

Remember to say what X and p stand for.

If the null hypothesis is true and the probability of 'heads' is actually 0.5 on each go, then the number of heads in 20 runs will have a binomial distribution with $n = 20$, $p = 0.5$. This can be written as follows:

If H_0 is true, $X \sim B(20, 0.5)$, where X is the number of 'heads' on 20 runs.

The cumulative binomial probability tables for $n = 20$, $p = 0.5$ are shown on the right.

n	x	0.050
20	0	
	1	0.0000
	2	0.0002
	3	0.0013
	4	0.0059
	5	0.0207
	6	0.0577
	7	0.1316
	8	0.2517
	9	0.4119
	10	0.5881
	11	0.7483
	12	0.8684
	13	0.9423
	14	0.9793
	15	0.9941
	16	0.9987
	17	0.9998
	18	1.0000
	19	
	20	

For a 2-tailed critical region at the 5% level of significance, you need 2.5% for each tail. The two tails are coloured in blue on this vertical line chart.

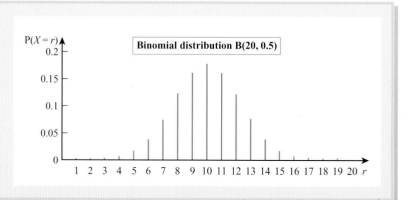

For the lower tail, look for a probability of 2.5%; it is unusual to be able to find exactly 2.5% so write down the one below 2.5% and the one above 2.5%.

$P(X \leqslant 5) = 0.0207 = 2.07\%$
$P(X \leqslant 6) = 0.0577 = 5.77\%$

> You need to write down both these probabilities so that it is clear how you chose your critical region.

The critical region for the lower tail is $X \leqslant 5$.

> Choose the one with a probability below 2.5% rather than the one with a probability above 2.5%.

For the upper tail, look for a probability of $100\% - 2.5\% = 97.5\%$. It is unusual to be able to find exactly 97.5% so write down the one below 97.5% and the one above 97.5%.

$P(X \leqslant 14) = 0.9793$
$P(X \leqslant 13) = 0.9423$

> You need to write down both these probabilities so that it is clear how you chose your critical region.

The upper tail consists of the high values with a total probability of 2.5%, or less.
Start with $P(X \leqslant 14) = 0.9793$ (the one above 97.5%) so
$1 - P(X \leqslant 14) = P(X \geqslant 15) = 1 - 0.9793 = 0.0207 = 2.07\%$.

> If X is **not** $\leqslant 14$, it could be 15, 16,..., 20.

The critical region for the upper tail is $X \geqslant 15$.

She should conclude the machine is biased if $X \leqslant 5$ or $X \geqslant 15$, where X is the number of 'heads' on 20 runs.

A ADVICE

- If H_0 is $p = 0.5$, the critical regions for the upper and lower tails are symmetrical.
- For a 2-tailed critical region, work out half the significance level and then carry on as if you were working out two separate critical regions: one for $H_1 : p < 0.5$ and one for $H_1 : p > 0.5$.

Critical region for an asymmetrical 2-tail test

EXAMPLE 2

A seed firm sells a particular variety of flower seeds which have an 85% germination rate. The seeds are expensive so they are stored in carefully controlled conditions. A batch of the seeds has been stored in different conditions and a sample of 19 from this batch is planted to see if the rate of germination has been affected.

i) What numbers of germinating seeds would lead to the conclusion, at the 10% significance level, that there has been a change in the germination rate?

ii) Hence, decide whether 18 seeds germinating would provide evidence of such a change.

SOLUTION

i) $H_0 : p = 0.85$
$H_1 : p \neq 0.85$ where p = proportion of the seeds in the batch that will germinate.

If the null hypothesis is true and the proportion of seeds in the batch germinating is indeed 0.85, the number of germinating seeds from a sample of 19 will have a binomial distribution with $n = 19$, $p = 0.85$.

This can be written as follows:

If H_0 is true, $X \sim B(19, 0.85)$, where X is the number of seeds in a sample of 19 that germinate.

> Write down the probability below 5% and the one above 5%.

The cumulative binomial probability tables for $n = 19$, $p = 0.85$ are shown.

For a 2-tailed critical region at the 10% level of significance, you need 5% for each tail.

$P(X \leqslant 12) = 0.0163 = 1.63\%$
$P(X \leqslant 13) = 0.0537 = 5.37\%$

> Choose the one with a probability below 5% rather than the one with a probability above 5%.

The critical region for the lower tail is $X \leqslant 12$. For the upper tail, look for a probability of $100\% - 5\% = 95\%$. It is unusual to be able to find exactly 95% so write down the one below 95% and the one above 95%.

$P(X \leqslant 18) = 0.9544$
$P(X \leqslant 17) = 0.8015$

> You need not spend time drawing a vertical line chart of the binomial distribution, but imagining it, or drawing a rough sketch, may help you understand the process.

You have not finished finding the upper tail yet. Start with the probability bigger than 95%.

n	x	p 0.850
19	0	
	1	
	2	
	3	
	4	
	5	
	6	
	7	
	8	0.0000
	9	0.0001
	10	0.0008
	11	0.0041
	12	0.0163
	13	0.0537
	14	0.1444
	15	0.3159
	16	0.5587
	17	0.8015
	18	0.9544
	19	1.0000

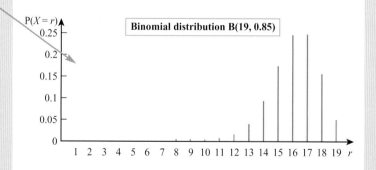

Binomial distribution B(19, 0.85)

> Not 18 or less means 19 or more.

$1 - P(X \leqslant 18) = P(X \geqslant 19) = 1 - 0.9544 = 0.0456 = 4.56\%$

The critical region for the upper tail is $X \geqslant 19$. This simplifies to $X = 19$ as only 19 seeds were planted so no more than 19 can germinate.

If 12 or fewer seeds germinate or if 19 seeds germinate, this will provide evidence, at the 10% level, that the germination rate has changed.

ii) 18 is not in the critical region so it does not provide evidence of a change at the 10% level.

LINKS
Statistics   Hypothesis testing (S2, S3 and S4).

Notice that the two parts of the critical region are not symmetrical.

Test Yourself ⊃**L**

For **questions 1 and 2**, X is the number of successes for a binomial random variable and p is the probability of success on each trial.

1 A sample size of 19 is taken to test the hypotheses $\left.\begin{array}{l} H_0 : p = 0.5 \\ H_1 : p \neq 0.5 \end{array}\right\}$ at the 1% level of significance.

   Which of the following gives the correct critical regions?
   A $X \leq 3, X \geq 15$ B $X \leq 3, X \geq 16$ C $X \leq 4, X \geq 15$
   D $X \leq 5, X \geq 14$ E $X \leq 5, X \geq 16$

2 A sample size of 14 is taken to test the hypotheses $\left.\begin{array}{l} H_0 : p > 0.6 \\ H_1 : p \neq 0.6 \end{array}\right\}$ at the 10% level of significance.
   Which of the following gives the correct critical regions?
   A $X \leq 4, X \geq 10$ B $X \leq 4, X \geq 11$ C $X \leq 4, X \geq 12$
   D $X \leq 5, X \geq 12$ E $X \leq 5, X \geq 13$

The following information is used in **questions 3 and 4**.

As part of a psychology experiment, a random sample of 18 people was asked to choose one of two puzzles: either a normal sudoku, using numbers, or a puzzle which used letters instead of numbers, but which was otherwise identical to the first one. The experimenter wanted to test whether there is a bias towards choosing either letters or numbers. The proportion of people in the population who would choose the puzzle with numbers is p. 13 people in the sample chose the puzzle with numbers. The test is conducted at the 5% level of significance.

3 Which of the following are the hypotheses for the test?
   A $H_0 : p > 0.5$ B $H_0 : p > 0.5$ C $H_0 : p = 0.5$ D $H_0 : p = 0.5$ E $H_0 : p \neq 0.5$
       $H_1 : p < 0.5$ $H_1 : p = 0.5$ $H_1 : p > 0.5$ $H_1 : p \neq 0.5$ $H_1 : p = 0.5$

Make sure you understand which are the correct hypotheses before attempting **question 4**.

4 Which of the following is the correct conclusion for the test? X is the number of people in a sample choosing the numbers puzzle.
   A The critical region is $X \leq 4, X \geq 13$ so there is evidence of a bias.
   B The critical region is $X \leq 4, X \geq 14$ so there is not sufficient evidence of a bias.
   C The critical region is $X \leq 4, X \geq 14$ so there is evidence of a bias.
   D The critical region is $4 \leq X \leq 13$ so there is not sufficient evidence of a bias.
   E The critical region is $X \leq 5, X \geq 13$ so there is evidence of a bias.

5 A teacher reads an article which says that 15% of the population are left handed. She wonders whether the proportion is the same among students taking A level Mathematics. She observes 19 students taking the C1 examination and notes how many of them are left handed (X). Assuming these 19 students are a random sample from the population of A level Mathematics students, what is the critical region for the test at the 5% level of significance?
   A $X \geq 4$ B $7 \leq X \leq 10$ C $X \geq 6$ D $X = 0, X \geq 7$ E $X \geq 7$

Exam-Style Question ⊃L

A national survey shows that 15% of young people are trying to give up smoking. A local health authority wants to investigate whether the proportion of young people in its area who are trying to give up smoking is 15% or whether it differs from this value. A random sample of 20 young people contains 1 who is trying to give up smoking.

i)   Write down suitable hypotheses.

ii)   What is the critical region for a suitable hypothesis test, at the 5% level?

iii)   Carry out the test, stating your conclusions clearly.

Index

Index

3 Natural logarithms and exponentials

Formulae and results

Here are some formulae and results which you will need to recall or derive for the S1 examination. There is an underlying assumption that students already know all the results needed for GCSE Mathematics. The following list is not exhaustive, and you should check with your teacher before your examination.

Samples

There are two notations, according to whether the data are grouped or not.

Ungrouped data

A sample has n observations of x, $x_1, x_2, \ldots x_n$.

Sample mean: $\bar{x} = \dfrac{\sum x_i}{n}$

Sum of squares of deviations:

$$S_{xx} = \sum(x_i - \bar{x})^2 = \sum x_i^2 - \frac{\left(\sum x_i\right)^2}{n} = \sum x_i^2 - n\bar{x}^2$$

Grouped data

A sample has n observations of x, with f_i observations of x_i. $\sum f_i = n$

Sample mean: $\bar{x} = \dfrac{\sum x_i f_i}{n}$

Sum of squares of deviations: $S_{xx} = \sum(x_i - \bar{x})^2 f_i$

$$= \sum x_i^2 f_i - \frac{\left(\sum x_i f_i\right)^2}{n} = \sum x_i^2 f_i - n\bar{x}^2$$

For both notations

Mean square deviation: $msd = \dfrac{S_{xx}}{n}$

Root mean square deviation: $rmsd = \sqrt{msd}$

Sample variance: $$s^2 = \frac{S_{xx}}{n-1}$$

Sample standard deviation: $$s = \sqrt{s^2}$$

Some calculators give both *rmsd* and *s*; make sure you understand the output from your calculator.

Coding

If $y = a + bx$ then $\bar{y} = a + b\bar{x}$ and $s_y^2 = b^2 s_x^2$

Selections and arrangements

Number of ways of
- arranging n unlike objects in line $= n!$
- selecting r objects from n unlike objects when the order does not matter
$$= {}^nC_r = \binom{n}{r} = \frac{n!}{r!(n-r)!}$$
- selecting r objects from n unlike objects when order does matter
$$= {}^nP_r = \frac{n!}{(n-r)!}$$

Conditional probability

$$P(B \mid A) = \frac{P(A \cap B)}{P(A)}$$

Discrete random variables

$$E(a + bX) = a + bE(X), \quad \text{Var}(a + bX) = b^2\text{Var}(X)$$

The binomial distribution

For the binomial distribution, B(n, p), the random variable, X, is the number of successes from n independent trials of a process for which P(success) $= p$.

$$P(X = r) = {}^nC_r p^r q^{n-r} \text{ for } r = 0, 1, 2, \ldots, n \text{ where } q = 1 - p.$$

The binomial hypothesis test

Null hypothesis	H_0:	The probability of the underlying population, p, has a given value
Alternative hypotheses	H_1:	$p \neq$ the given value (2-tail test)
	or	$p >$ the given value (1-tail test)
	or	$p <$ the given value (1-tail test)
Test statistic		Observed number of successes in a sample of size n trials
Critical values		Can be calculated, or derived from cumulative frequency tables